National Institute for Social Work
Research Unit

Better for the Break

ENID LEVIN, JO MORIARTY
and PETER GORBACH

London: HMSO

ISBN 011 7017760

The views expressed in this report are those of the authors, and do not
necessarily reflect the views of the Department of Health.

National Institute for Social Work
5 Tavistock Place
London WC1H 9SN
Telephone: 071 387 9681

Contents

Acknowledgements

We are grateful to the Research and Development Division of the Department of Health for financing this research, and for the successive contributions made by each of the principal research officers: Sue Moylan, Madeleine Simms and Ruth Chadwick.

Consistently through the project we have received constructive advice and support from the Advisory Committee of: Professor Anthony Mann, Dr Ruth Chadwick, Dr Roger Gibbins, Dr Ann Netten, Mr Michael Power, and Professor Ian Sinclair.

Colleagues within the Research Unit have also made a contribution which this acknowledgement can only begin to recognise; we thank them all for their patience and interest.

Over the course of the project we received administrative and secretarial help from Cheryl Clarke, Tina O'Regan, Connetta Smith, Chrissie Poole and Kay Thompson. Successive unit programmers Shahid Akudi, Roger Bowater, Anwar Hussein, Farzana Majid and Yoga Sivagurunathan helped with preparing and analysing the data. Dr Robert Power was a researcher at the pilot stage and Jill Mortimer coded the follow up interviews.

In the process of turning the report into this book, we should particularly thank the Unit Director, Dr Jan Pahl, for her advice and support, Chrissie Poole and Connetta Smith for their word processing skills and their patience, and Toby Andrew and Yoga Sivagurunathan for their help with the analyses and tables. We are grateful to Dr Peter Rea for compiling the index.

Within the Institute we should like to thank the Director, Daphne Statham, for her encouragement. The Library and Information Service headed by Guistina Ryan and latterly John McTernan, and also Sue Jardine, Hannah Madgwick, Mavis Taylor, Angela Upton and Mark Watson have been sedulous and patient in their help.

We feel fortunate to have had such a reliable and hardworking team of interviewers. At various times, we received help from Carolyn Adcock, Pat Asher, Verna Beckford, Marian Billings, Marie Carroll, Frances Duncan, Dora Ellaby, Lynda Heley, Rosemary Johnson, Diana Kent, Sylvia McReynolds, Emily Platt, Kay Taylor and Lorna Wake.

Although staff in the study and pilot areas from health and social services and voluntary organisations must remain anonymous, they themselves can measure their contribution in terms of forms completed, telephone calls answered, visits received, and families contacted.

Finally, the help of everyone above would have counted for nothing, had we not had the privilege of hearing the views of all the carers and elderly people in the sample whom we interviewed. That they should have set aside their time, shown such hospitality, and shared their thoughts and experiences so frankly and clearly meets with our admiration and gratitude.

List of Tables

List of Figures

1   Introduction to the Study

I've been told he has Alzheimer's disease .... I'd like to wave a wand over him and make him better but I suppose I've accepted it .... Had I not had the support [of the sitter] .... I would feel very frustrated.

Background

This book is based upon a study of respite services for the carers of confused elderly people. The research was commissioned by the Department of Health and carried out by the National Institute for Social Work Research Unit (Levin and Moriarty, 1990; Levin *et al.*, 1992).

There is a growing literature that documents the problems and stresses experienced by the carers of elderly people. Four reviews assess current British research on these carers and on the services provided for them (Parker, 1990; Sinclair *et al.*, 1990; Twigg *et al.*, 1990; Twigg, 1992). They rightly single out the carers of elderly people with dementia as a group whose need for support requires special attention. A recent community survey has shown that, in general, caring for a person with dementia is a greater source of stress than caring for a person without dementia, and that caring for a person with moderate to severe dementia is a greater source of stress than caring for a person with mild dementia (O'Connor *et al.*, 1990).

The care of elderly people with dementia has implications for services as well as for families. These elderly people make heavier use of services than others (Livingston *et al.*, 1990; O'Connor *et al.*, 1989). However, the effects of different types and combinations of services have not been widely evaluated.

The first study by the National Institute for Social Work (NISW) of the carers of confused elderly people confirmed that elderly people with dementia were more likely to enter residential care than others. Moreover, it showed that, where no more than standard services were provided, the psychological health of the carers improved, on average, if the elderly person was admitted to permanent residential care (Levin *et al.*, 1989). More encouragingly, the first NISW study suggested that community services were relevant to the carers' problems, appreciated where used, and could have beneficial effects on the psychological health of some carers. It raised issues, however, about respite services,

[1]

which included their availability, the targeting of such services, and their effects on the elderly people and the carers.

These issues required further study, and in 1988 the Department of Health funded the NISW researchers to conduct a programme of work on respite services for carers who lived in the same household as the confused elderly person whom they looked after.

Before we describe the study, we must define the term 'respite', because it has come to have more than one meaning when used to describe services. For example, it is often used to refer only to short stays in residential care for elderly people. In this book, we use the term respite services to cover any service which looks after elderly people temporarily, so that their carers are given a break. Thus the respite services considered in this book are day care, sitting and carers' support services, and relief care in homes, hospital or family settings.

Aims

The main aims of the study were:

First, to establish and compare the characteristics and problems of groups of confused elderly people and their carers using different types and mixes of respite services.

Second, to elicit the carers', elderly people's and practitioners' views of these services so that guidelines for practice can be based upon them.

And third, to examine the effectiveness of different types and mixes of respite services in terms of their acceptability, their impact on the carers' psychological health, their impact on the elderly people, and their effects on the admission of the elderly people to permanent residential care.

Methods

The project was undertaken in collaboration with the staff of health, social services and voluntary organisations in three parts of England.

In selecting the areas, we sought to ensure that sitting and carer support schemes, as well as day and relief care services, operated in the areas, that service providers in all sectors would be willing to work with us, and that, as far as possible, the study areas were geographically widely dispersed. We were successful in meeting these criteria: Area One is part of a city in a southern county; Area Two is comprised of small towns and villages in a county in the Midlands; and Area Three is part of a city in a northern Metropolitan District.

In order to obtain the formal permissions and the co-operation necessary for the research, the preparatory stage of the project in 1988 involved over 50 discussions and interviews with service providers in the areas. After piloting in one area, fieldwork began in 1989 and was completed in 1991. In broad outline, it was conducted in three stages: these were, first, a survey of confused elderly people known to the arrangers and providers of respite services, second, interviews with a random sample of elderly people and their carers known to respite services, and third, follow up interviews with the carers about one year later. It must be stated that the extent and nature of respite provision does vary throughout the country. In one sense, therefore, we could not seek to suggest that the results from the study can be generalised. However, it is worth making the point that we looked at the types of service which are to be found more generally rather than at intensely specialist and localised schemes.

The initial survey

The sample was to include both carers who were using respite services and those who were not using them. It was also to include those currently known to services and those referred to services over a fixed period. We therefore began by asking the arrangers and providers of respite services across the study areas to complete a form providing brief details on each confused person, aged 65 or over and living with at least one other person, who was using their service or known to them on March 1st 1989. As well as asking about age and gender, we asked a set of six screening questions about the elderly people's problems with memory and orientation (Levin *et al.*, 1989). In over three quarters of the cases, the professional completing the form was able to confirm that he or she knew that the elderly person had a recognised diagnosis of dementia.

These forms were completed by heads of day and relief care programmes, co-ordinators of sitting and carers' support schemes, psychogeriatricians, geriatricians, community psychiatric nurses and social workers. We then maintained regular contact with these service providers over a fixed period to collect forms on elderly people recently referred to them.

A total of 691 returns on 530 elderly people were received during the period of study. After careful consideration of the distribution of the elderly people identified in the initial survey across the services providing breaks, we decided to adopt a simple random procedure for picking the sample of current users from these returns. We then picked further random samples of users from the returns subsequently received.

Of the 530 persons identified, eight per cent were excluded on grounds of age or place of residence, 30 per cent were excluded because the elderly people had died or entered residential care before their carers could be interviewed, and 55 per cent participated in the interview survey. An additional number (*n*=12) were selected for pilot interviews. Seven per cent of the carers in the survey population declined to be interviewed (*n*=37). This figure rises to 11 per cent if we include only those carers whom we requested to interview, but, with 89 per cent agreeing, the refusal rate is still very low. Compared with other carers, it appeared that sons were less willing to be interviewed. Nevertheless it is important to bear in mind that they constituted only eight per cent in total of all those carers whom we asked to participate. Comparisons of the rest of the survey population with those who were interviewed showed that they did not differ in terms of whether or not a diagnosis of dementia had been reported, their gender and their living arrangements. The proportion of elderly people from each study area in the sample was similar to the distribution in the study population as a whole. However, those elderly people who died before their carers could be approached were slightly older and had a higher number of memory and orientation problems than those who were interviewed. Attrition rates attributable to death are, of course, to be expected in samples such as these.

As can be seen, the sample is a services sample rather than a community sample. We believe that this sample is adequate for the purposes for which it was intended, that is, to examine the factors associated with the use of respite services in three areas and to assess the effects of these services upon the elderly people and their carers.

The first interview survey

Once an elderly person had been identified for inclusion in the main survey, we asked the practitioner who had filled in the form to approach the carer and find out whether he or she would be willing to participate in the study; subject to this agreement, the name and address of the family was then given to us. Interviews were obtained for a total of 292 carers. Five of these have been excluded from the analyses because the carers were found at the interview to be looking after an elderly person who lived alone. The report therefore concentrates on the 287 carers who lived with the person for whom they cared. Of these carers, 58 per cent were identified in the first survey of people using respite services on March 1st 1989, and 42 per cent were identified from the forms completed in subsequent months on people newly referred to services.

The carers and the elderly people were visited by one of the 14 interviewers recruited, trained and managed by the research team. One of the researchers interviewed over 50 of the families either on her own or with each interviewer to provide a means of checking that consistency in interviewing method was maintained. The structured interviews with the carers lasted, on average, about two hours.

The interviews with the carers provided a very detailed picture of the circumstances in which they cared, of the help they gave the elderly people, of the services that they used, and of their views of these services. The 28 item version of the General Health Questionnaire (GHQ) (Goldberg, 1978) and the SELFCARE (D) (Bird *et al.*, 1987) were completed by the carers to provide a means of assessing their psychological health. The carers' ethnicity was documented.

The interviews with the elderly people were shorter and some parts required corroboration from the carers. They included questions on their physical and mental state, and, where possible, on the elderly people's views of the services. The carers filled in the Behaviour Rating Scale from the Clifton Assessment Procedures for the Elderly (CAPE) (Pattie and Gilleard, 1979), and the Depressive Signs Scale (DSS) (Katona and Aldridge, 1985). The elderly people were asked the questions which make up the CAPE Information and Orientation Test.

The follow-up interview survey

We established outcomes for the 287 elderly people in terms of whether they were still at home, had died, or entered residential care, about one year after the first interviews. At this stage, 243 carers (85 per cent) were interviewed again. The carers filled in the GHQ, the SELFCARE (D) and the CAPE Behaviour Rating Scale again, so that changes in their psychological health and in the level of the elderly people's dependency could be examined. They were also questioned about their experiences of caring and about changes in their use of services since the first interview.

Structure of the book

We begin in Chapter Two by identifying the primary carers and what their responsibilities involved. In Chapter Three, we discuss the roles of doctors, social workers and community psychiatric nurses in assessment and long term care management. In Chapter Four, we compare the users of the various packages of respite. In Chapters Five, Six and Seven, we consider day care, sitting and carers support services, and relief care separately. We raise issues about improving the delivery of these services at the end of these chapters. In Chapter Eight, we go on to summarise the main findings on outcomes and the results of our analyses of the effectiveness of services to date. In our conclusions, we restate the case for providing respite services and make suggestions on arranging and providing services.

Finally, we should like to make the point that, by changing the names of each carer and elderly person, we have sought to maintain their anonymity while preserving the value of their comments. These comments, stemming from their everyday experiences, can have no substitute in helping to identify and clarify ways in which services have helped and ways in which they can be improved.

2   Who Cared and What was Involved

I promised to look after her in sickness and in health and I'll keep my side of the bargain.

Introduction

The theme of this chapter is the relationship between the carers and elderly people and the nature of the care provided. There are two important preliminary points about the sample. The first is that the carers were living in the same household as the person they cared for, and so were committed to caring on a daily basis. The second is that, by virtue of the elderly people's condition, they were involved in meeting a complex set of needs, both physical and psychological. The combination of time spent on caring and the amount of help provided meant that the carers' role was a particularly intensive one.

Our purpose is to outline the sample characteristics prior to discussing the role of services in later chapters. We recognise that this approach may be at the expense of neglecting some of the positive aspects of caring. Additionally, we are not seeking to imply that the relationship between carer and cared for was simply one of one person being dependent upon another. Instead, our emphasis will be upon drawing together those threads which we hope will improve our understanding of the question: what is the relevance of respite services for carers of confused elderly people?

Previous work on caring

Much of the earliest research on caring was undertaken by feminists who identified the way in which caring was perceived as a low status activity and characterised by strong gender divisions, with women carers outnumbering men considerably (Dalley, 1988; Finch and Groves, 1983). This variation is partly accounted for by the higher numbers of women caring for someone outside their own household (Green, 1988).

A consistent picture has emerged of the circumstances in which caring is likely to be necessary: the key indicator of the receipt of help from family and friends is an inability to deal with activities of daily living, such as washing and bathing, dressing and mobility (Chappell and

Blandford, 1991; Noelker and Bass, 1989; Vetter *et al.*, 1992). Furthermore, where this sort of personal care is required it is family members, rather than friends or neighbours, who are providing the assistance (Wenger, 1992).

As increasing recognition has been given to the contribution of family members as carers, so too anxieties have arisen that rising divorce rates and increased paid employment for women might affect the number of daughters available to care (sic) - this was indeed the starting point for the inclusion of questions on caring responsibilities in the 1985 General Household Survey, the results of which have proved to be so seminal to later work (Green, 1988). Investigation of the extent of co-residence between adult children and their elderly parents raises the possibility that such assumptions may be premature (Grundy and Harrop, 1992). Furthermore, the phenomenon of reconstituted households (for instance, where a divorced daughter invites her widowed mother to live with her) has also been noted (Lewis and Meredith, 1988).

Household structures have proved to be a useful way of examining caring circumstances. This has enabled a key distinction to be made between the *larger* numbers of people caring for someone in a separate household with the *smaller* number of co-resident carers (those people living in the same household as the person for whom they care), who account for a far greater proportion of the amount of care provided. Arber and Ginn's (1991) secondary analysis of the General Household Survey data for 1985 concluded that, on average, co-resident carers spent 53 hours per week on caring, compared with an equivalent figure among non-resident carers of nine hours. The greatest time was allocated by carers who supported their elderly spouse (65 hours). Moreover, almost half of this co-resident care was being provided by people who were elderly themselves.

The next step from examining the household circumstances in which caring takes place is to identify the relationships between carers and those for whom they care. Some studies have used the term hierarchy of preferences, or obligations, to categorise the principles determining the process by which an individual assumes the care of an older person (Qureshi and Walker, 1989; Ungerson, 1987). Taken simply, for married people, a spouse would be the first source of support. Next, the parent-child relationship would operate with, in the case of elderly people, adult children caring for parents. Then, might come membership of the same household, where an adult child would undertake more care than his or her non-resident siblings. Finally, gender would play a part with an assumption that a daughter in law might be preferred to a son (Finch, 1989). Finch and Mason (1993) prefer the term *responsibilities* to obligations. In their study, they found that among those who were interviewed, there was a rejection of the notion of a 'right' to expect assistance from relatives; rather that such assistance stemmed from a developing, often reciprocated, commitment over time.

How the factors outlined above may operate in practice was clearly demonstrated by Sinclair *et al.* (1990). This review concluded that most elderly people requiring help were cared for by spouses or children and the majority of such help was provided by *one person alone*. A study of elderly people over the age of 75 known to social services departments in three areas of England emphasised that their social networks were very small. Not every person had an identified carer and, even among those who did, if they were childless, widowed, or had other family members living some distance away, the question of whether there was anyone else available to help was quite academic (Allen *et al.*, 1992).

Socio-economic status and costs of caring

In the context of the high proportion of elderly spouses among co-resident carers, it is worth making the general point that, compared with other age groups in the population, people over the age of 60 are over-represented in the lower income bands. Older married couple households fare particularly badly (Askham *et al.*, 1992).

The 1985 General Household Survey data suggested that there was little variation between the percentages of carers in non-manual and manual socio-economic groups or between groups with differing levels of educational qualifications (Green, 1988). Notwithstanding this, there are limitations to analyses based upon traditional stratifications. First, as we have seen, many carers are beyond the statutory retirement age. Second, resources may not be shared equally within the household (Pahl, 1989*a*).

Recognition of such shortcomings has led to a focus upon alternative ways to measure the financial impact of caring. Apart from direct costs, such as extra food, clothing or heating requirements, it is also essential to consider the opportunity costs of, for instance, being unable to take up or maintain paid employment. One survey of members of the Carers National Association (CNA) revealed that less than 40 per cent of the respondents under the age of 55 were in paid employment (CNA, 1992).

The introduction of Invalid Care Allowance (ICA) for carers of working age signalled that the social security system officially acknowledged the impact of caring responsibilities upon the prospect of paid employment. However, two particular problems remain. The first is that of non-eligibility because of the level of the earnings limit, even where paid employment and earnings have been substantially affected. The second is delayed take up, probably attributable to unawareness of the benefit's existence (McLaughlin, 1991).

Glendinning (1992) also concluded that social security provision for carers, while improved, remains inadequate. The age limits for ICA mean that carers over pensionable age receive no recognition for themselves. Further exclusions come with its linking to

Attendance/Disability Living Allowance. Options which may develop further in the future, such as career breaks, flexible working patterns and workplace arrangements, have their possibilities but a glaring limitation continues to be the actual level of ICA. Furthermore, it can only be claimed by carers who have very low incomes from paid employment. Nor does it offer any real advantages to claimant households (other than the payment of National Insurance Contributions) because it is taken into account for means tested benefits.

The relationship between caring and stress

Until this point, we have discussed work on caring in very general terms. A specific purpose of many studies has been to examine the relationship between the various components of caring and attitudes towards their delivery, in particular the relationship between caring and stress, what happens in those circumstances in which:

> *Caregiving, which previously might have been but one fleeting component of an encompassing relationship, can now come to be the dominant, overriding component.....to the point where it occupies the entirety of the relationship.*
> (Pearlin *et al.*, 1990, p.583)

The distinction made in the earliest studies between the *objective* difficulties, such as the physical workload involved in caring, and the *subjective* responses to this situation, in the form of the impact these have upon the carers' morale or perceived levels of stress, has continued to play an important role, as reviews of the literature have shown (Morris *et al.*, 1989; Vitaliano *et al.*, 1991).

Given that individuals' responses to similar caring situations will not be the same, how do we find a way of explaining any disparities? Here, the task has centred around an examination of factors which might act as mediators between the process of caring and its impact.

This has resulted in the development of a number of theoretical frameworks, often reflecting diverse, sometimes conflicting, findings. What are the reasons for this? One plausible explanation may lie in the differing ways in which caring has been conceptualised. Some studies have applied very broad definitions of caring, using it to include any assistance with daily routines, such as shopping. Others have interpreted caring more rigorously, insisting it encompasses far more intensive assistance (Zarit and Teri, 1991).

A second possible cause stems from sampling differences. It is important to recognise that studies which have used self-selected samples of carers are likely to differ from those using samples which have been recruited by other means. Zarit and Teri (1991) go on to cite the salutary example of a study which found that the number of people who *failed* to identify themselves as carers - despite meeting the necessary criteria - was as large as those who did!

Two of the most frequent themes in the literature have centred around gender differences and coping strategies. A study of adult children in the United States showed that the lack of an adequate social support network predicted anxiety among men, but not women. For the women, a feeling that they had no control over the caring situation was the most important predictor of distress (Parks and Pilusik, 1991). A study of spouses of people with Alzheimer's disease reported that men showed higher levels of well-being than women and that positive focus as a coping strategy accounted for the greatest proportion of variance in well-being (Borden, 1991).

Social support has also been felt to affect carers' responses. Perceptions of the need for more assistance from friends and relatives was reported to be strongly associated with higher stress levels, use of psychotropic medication, affect, and satisfaction with life (Gwyther and George, 1986). Sistler (1989) took a more circumspect approach, concluding that as a coping strategy, the seeking of social support did not predict carers' subjective well-being. Social workers should, she suggested, instead focus not upon encouraging carers to seek social support, the *process*, but upon the *product* of social support - other people's response to the carer, for instance, in the form of visits.

The conflict that can arise if there are conflicting or multiple roles, such as being a carer, spouse, and paid employee has also been explored. One study from the United States suggested that role strain models for African-American and white women differ (Mui, 1992). Role theory has been discussed in relation to gender differences (Miller and Cafassa, 1992).

The quality of past relationships has also been believed to play a role. Levin *et al.* (1989) suggested that carers who had not felt close to the person they cared for before his or her illness had developed were more than twice as likely to want him or her to enter residential care permanently. Springer and Brubaker (1984), writing especially for a readership of carers, pointed out that the dynamics of caring are such that they have the potential to create new conflicts and also to deepen older ones.

So far, we have said little about the association between carer stress and the characteristics of those cared for. Some studies, especially those of heterogeneous samples, have suggested that these have only limited direct impact. Nolan and Grant (1992) argued it was not the degree of physical care required, the levels of incontinence, or presence of confused and difficult behaviour that accounted for psychological malaise but the carer's reactions to caring. In a sample of people caring for a relative with dementia, Gilhooly (1984) found that the only characteristic of the person cared for which was significantly correlated with morale was gender - those caring for women were in higher morale. However, others have found stronger relationships. Eagles *et al.* (1987) showed that relatives of people with dementia showed more *stress*, although they were no more likely to show signs of psychiatric morbidity than those caring for people who did not have dementia.

The particular problems which have been shown to be associated with lack of well-being in carers are incontinence, disturbance at night, and the need for constant supervision (Gilleard *et al.*, 1984; Levin *et al.*, 1989). In a community sample of 120 people over the age of 75, O'Connor *et al.* (1990) found that reported problems and stress in the carer increased with the severity of the dementia syndrome. Recurring passive behavioural problems, such as apathy, were better tolerated than physical dependence or the more disruptive problems, such as constantly demanding attention.

Furthermore, the frequency with which carers may be faced with such situations should not be underestimated. A study of 178 patients in contact with community and in-patient services in one health authority concluded both that behavioural problems occurred in a significant proportion of those with Alzheimer's disease and also that the majority of these disturbances were directly associated with more severe disease, as measured in terms of cognitive function and overall severity (Burns *et al.*, 1990). In this context, it has been suggested that the *absence* of certain behavioural problems may prove to be an important factor in determining both carer well-being and the success of community care (Hinchcliffe *et al.*, 1992).

Elder abuse

In recent years, this topic has received increasing, often sensationalised attention. Much of the earliest work in this area was North American in origin and, in Britain, systematically collected information about the forms and prevalence of abuse remains limited. This was the raison d'être behind McCreadie's seminal work in 1991.

A recent Social Services Inspectorate (SSI) publication (1992) quoted the following definition as helpful:

> *...the physical, emotional or psychological abuse of an older person by a formal or informal carer. The abuse is repeated and is the violation of a person's human and civil rights by a person or persons who have power over the life of a dependent.*
> (Eastman, 1984, cited in SSI, 1992, p.7)

Based upon the accounts of staff working in social services departments in two London boroughs, the SSI study classified abuse as physical, psychological (verbal aggression, humiliating behaviour and so on), financial, sexual, and neglect (the deliberate refusal to meet basic needs). Although physical abuse was the most frequently reported type of abuse, half of the 64 cases involved more than one type of abuse. Often the abuse was longstanding and seemed to be more frequent where the abused person was more dependent and cared for by a co-resident carer.

An earlier study looked at patients referred to geriatric services for respite care over a six month period (Homer and Gilleard, 1990). Almost half of the 51 carers interviewed admitted to some form of abuse. Significant risk factors were a poor relationship prior to the patient's illness and previous abuse over many years. Carers who admitted to physical or verbal abuse scored highly on the depression subscale of the GHQ28 (Goldberg and Williams, 1988) and rated the person they cared for as having more socially disturbed behaviour and presenting greater communication problems. In terms of predicting physical abuse, the most significant factor was the carer's levels of alcohol consumption.

A study of 184 people with Alzheimer's disease in the United States examined the issue from the perspective of the patient-carer dyad, treating violence from one towards the other in conjunction (Paveza *et al.*, 1992). Family violence was associated with two variables. The first was depression in the carer - particularly at levels where the person was likely to meet the criteria for a clinical diagnosis. The second was that of living arrangements; patients living with family but without a spouse were almost three times more likely to be at risk than those in other types of household.

Previous work at NISW emphasised that those carers who reported hitting, shaking, slapping or pushing their relatives were in a clear minority (Levin *et al.*, 1989). Often, the person they cared for had hit out at them. Carers who reported losing their temper were particularly likely to be looking after a person who had problems communicating, disturbed them at night and behaviour such as following the carer around or asking the same question repeatedly. Their own reaction in these situations was a source of great distress to the carers.

Although this issue requires further research, there are clear methodological problems surrounding both the potential under-reporting of sensitive topics and ethical considerations. These will continue to prove difficult to address, as was made apparent in a recent study (Ogg and Bennett, 1992).

The sample in context

As we go on to describe the characteristics of the carers and elderly people, it will become clear that our perspective is sharply focussed upon those themes which are especially apt where carers live in the same household as someone with Alzheimer's disease or a related disorder. Our prime purpose is to emphasise the degree of help required by the elderly people in the sample and the impact that this had upon the lives of their carers.

The characteristics of the carers

Relationship to the elderly person

By far the largest proportion of carers in the sample was made up of spouses and daughters, as is shown in Table 2.1 below. This is an important point because, as we shall show, the distribution of the age, gender and living arrangements among the carers in the sample was explained by a large extent by their relationship to the person cared for.

Table 2.1 Relationship of Carer to Elderly Person

	Sample %	Total N
Wife	33	96
Husband	24	70
Daughter	22	62
Son	6	16
Daughter in law	6	17
Sister	4	10
Brother	1	3
Other	4	13
Total	**100**	**287**

While wives outnumbered husbands, the most noticeable difference was the number of daughters, forming the third largest group, when compared with other relations such as sons or siblings. The daughters comprised the most varied sub group within the sample. Around a quarter were single; nearly everyone in this group had lived with the elderly person virtually all their lives. An identical number were widowed, divorced or separated and had invited the elderly person to move into their home or had moved to the parental home themselves. The remaining 52 per cent were married and lived with their husband, the elderly person, and (in about half the cases) adult children.

Almost without exception, where the elderly person lived with a married son, it was not the son but the daughter in law who had taken on the position of the primary carer. In these families, the son was often an only child or had no sisters. Even where this was not the case, some daughter in law carers stated that there was little contact, or even bad feeling, between their husband and his siblings.

By contrast, where sons were primary carers, they were much more likely to have never been married. Almost all had lived with the elderly person since birth.

The final group of carers, while numerically small, was important in terms of explaining that blood relationship alone was not the only reason for a person to have assumed the role of carer; two granddaughters cared for the grandmothers who had brought them up; a niece did the same for her aunt (to the extent that during the interview she referred to her aunt both as aunt and mother).

Ethnicity

Despite the existence of longstanding minority ethnic communities in two of the study areas, all 287 carers and the people for whom they cared were white Europeans.

Gender

The influence of relationship and household composition meant that it was unsurprising that almost 70 per cent of the sample were women.

Among the men who cared *irrespective of kinship tie*, there were just three exceptions to the pattern where the household consisted only of themselves and the person for whom they cared. In these three instances, the carer's wife was in paid employment. First, a self employed son looked after his father. Second, a recently married son looked after his mother. Lastly, a son in law on long term sick leave looked after his wife's father.

Six daughters described themselves as their mother's primary carer while living in the same household as their father. In these cases, their father's general health was such that it seemed they had to give some degree of care to *both* parents.

Age

Two-thirds of the carers were over the age of 65. The eldest carer was a 92 year old man looking after his wife and the youngest a woman of 23 who cared for her mother in law. Given the predominance of husbands among the men who cared, this accounted for why they were much more likely to be older. Their mean age was 72, compared with 64 for the women. The mean age of the sample overall was 66.

Health

The General Household Survey (GHS) 1988 (Office of Population Censuses and Surveys, 1990) suggested that the prevalence of chronic illness was strongly related to age. Forty per cent of the GHS respondents in the 65-74 age group reported a limiting longstanding illness. Forty seven per cent of the carers in our sample in this age group

Figure 2.1 Age Distribution of the Carers by Gender

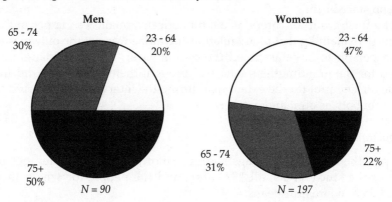

reported a longstanding illness when asked a similar question. The percentage rose to 63 per cent for the over 75s. Age related health conditions such as arthritis, hypertension or other cardiovascular problems were among those problems mentioned most often. Over a third of the carers rated their health as good and this did not vary by age.

Admittedly this information was limited by its reliance upon self report. However, we also asked the carers whether they were currently taking any medication. The numbers of carers taking analgesia, anti-inflammatory drugs, diuretics and so on suggested that it was reasonable to set some store by the carers' assessments of their health status.

Furthermore, we believe that it is important to pay some attention to the issue of the carers' health because, as we shall show, for men in particular this proved to be an important factor influencing outcome.

Living arrangements

Almost three-quarters of the households in the sample consisted of the carer (usually a spouse) and the elderly person alone. Just under 20 per cent of households consisted of three people. Here, by contrast, the elderly person was most usually living with an adult child and the child's spouse although in some cases they comprised the elderly person, spouse, and child. The few remaining households in the sample contained four or more people. For instance, one wife looking after her husband shared the home with her daughter and granddaughter.

There was a clear association between the size of these households and the length of time which they had existed. Given that so many households comprising two people were made up of spouses or single children and the parent they cared for, it was unsurprising that almost all had been established for at least 25 years.

Nearly all of the households of less than five years standing consisted of those where the carer was the elderly person's daughter or daughter in law. This is in keeping with the generally accepted picture that it is only with increasing disability that elderly people move in with their adult children.

Across all types of household, more than two thirds of the carers had lived with the person for whom they cared for over 25 years. The longest time together was that of two sisters who had lived together all their lives (84 years). One husband, married for 43 years himself, showed how this could influence his attitude to caring:

> *After you've been together all these years, [you should] have a go at it and see if you can do it.*

Employment status

Only 17 per cent of the sample as a whole were in paid employment. This was almost equally divided between those who were working full and part time. Although two-thirds of the sample were over retirement age there are good reasons for not excluding them from all the discussion on employment status. First, we should recognise that some carers over the age of retirement at the time that they were interviewed had given up work early in order that they might look after the elderly person. Second, of those carers in paid employment, 25 per cent were aged 60 or over.

If we do exclude those carers over the age of retirement at the time that they were first interviewed, the percentage of carers in paid employment rises to 43 per cent. At the same time, the number of carers who attributed their absence of paid employment to their position as a carer increases from 27 per cent of the overall sample not in paid work to 84 per cent of those under the age of retirement.

Twenty five per cent of the carers in paid employment reported that they had had problems because of their responsibilities as a carer. One daughter, employed full time and interviewed while her mother spent a fortnight in a local authority home, made clear:

> *[I] have to go late and come home early on the days [mother is] not at day care. I fit [my] hours around her day care. Luckily I can do this in my job, but now she is in relief care I'm putting a lot of hours in at work, including weekends.*

For others, such as one wife in her early sixties who worked part time as a cleaner, her employment provided a source of income and chance to switch off from the role of caring:

> *Work - that's my pleasure, I enjoy going to work!*

Socio-economic status

The sample contained carers with diverse backgrounds. Many had held jobs which reflected the industries which had predominated in the study areas and this may account for the greater number of non manual workers in Area One than in the other two areas. Two-thirds of the carers were owner occupiers, a similar picture to that in the population over 60 as a whole (Askham *et al.*, 1992).

Financial issues and caring

Just under half of the carers mentioned that they had incurred extra expenditure or experienced reduced income over the past year. Of these, three quarters ascribed this to meeting the needs of the elderly person; extra heating costs and replacements for clothing due to incontinence were mentioned most frequently. Twelve per cent of the carers caring for someone who wore incontinence pads had to pay for the pads themselves. There were also the sorts of cost which might arise sporadically but nonetheless could be considerable. One daughter reported that her mother blocked the lavatory with an incontinence pad one Sunday morning. The plumber's bill amounted to £150.

Seventy per cent of the elderly people received Disability Living/Attendance Allowance, almost evenly divided between the higher and lower rates. Few carers of people *not* receiving the allowance were unfamiliar with it but only 26 per cent had ever applied. This was a matter of some concern as, on the basis of the elderly people's dependency, it is probable that nearly all would have met the criteria.

Thirty four per cent of the carers below retirement age claimed Invalid Care Allowance (ICA). Remembering that so few carers were in paid employment (or indeed that some may have preferred to devote their attention to caring), it was regrettable that, almost half of those not claiming ICA stated that they had never heard of the benefit. Two carers received payments from the Independent Living Fund which was set up during the course of the study. We did not ask about receipt of the carer's premium because we did not ask carers whether they were on Income Support. Some carers specifically mentioned that, once they received ICA, their Income Support had been reduced.

The characteristics of the elderly people

Gender

Among the elderly people, the ratio of women to men was 3:2. This reflects the nature of the sample, and is consistent with the pattern that women tend to live longer than men and to marry men older than themselves.

The women were almost equally divided between those who were cared for by their husbands and those cared for by a daughter or daughter in law. Most of the men were cared for by their wives. It was particularly unusual for an elderly man to be cared for by his son; there were only three in the sample altogether.

Age

Discussion of the age of the elderly people must be prefaced by recognition that the prevalence of dementia increases with age. Just under three-quarters of the elderly people were aged over 75, as is shown in more detail in Figure 2.2. The women were more likely to be older than the men. Their mean age was 80, compared with that of 77 for men. The overall mean age of the sample was 79.

Figure 2.2 Age Distribution of the Elderly People by Gender

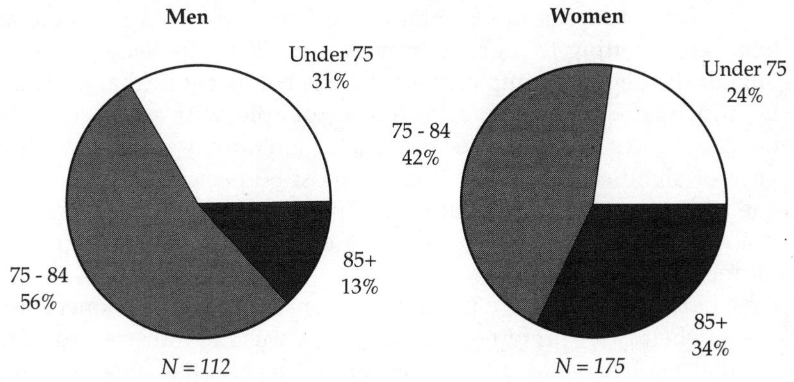

Men

Under 75
31%

75 - 84
42%

75 - 84
56%

85+
13%

N = 112

Women

Under 75
24%

85+
34%

N = 175

Assessment of the elderly people

We used several ways to assess the level of help the elderly people required. The one which we shall refer to most often consisted of the Behaviour Rating Scale (BRS) from the Clifton Assessment Procedures for the Elderly (CAPE) (Pattie and Gilleard, 1979). This is a widely used measure which is relatively simple and quick to complete. It consists of 18 items. The scores are then graded from A to E. Grade A encompasses those with the lowest scores (0-3); these are people who are almost completely independent. By contrast, people rated as having a grade E dependency (18+) have requirements which are comparable with the type of help needed by residents in a continuing care setting. It has been noted that there does appear to be a 'ceiling effect' with the BRS (Blessed *et al.*, 1991). Figure 2.3 shows that, on the basis of this measure, almost three quarters of the elderly people were highly or maximally dependent.

Figure 2.3 The Elderly People's Scores on the CAPE

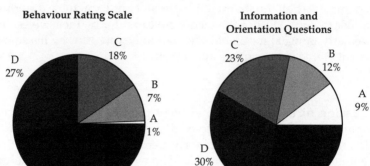

The interviewers also assessed the elderly people's cognitive state using the Information and Orientation Test from the CAPE. There are 12 items contributing to a grade from A to E. Here the *lower* the score the higher the degree of impairment. Scores below eight (that is, grades C, D, and E) are usually found among people with a diagnosis of dementia. Scores of eight and above are generally associated with an absence of significant deterioration. Almost 80 per cent of the elderly people had scores below the cut off point. The mean score was 5.2 but over a quarter scored two or less, the score indicating the greatest impairment.

Some elderly people were unwilling or unable to be questioned. In a few cases, their carer preferred that he or she was not interviewed. This meant that we had valid Information and Orientation scores for 258 of the elderly people, 90 per cent of the sample. Looking at the characteristics of those who were not questioned, it seems probable that they were likely to have been included in the largest categories, marked or severe impairment, and so we think it reasonable to assume that, had we obtained scores for these people too, this would not have altered the picture.

As an additional measure, we asked the carer whether the elderly person experienced any of the NISW Six Noticeable Problems (Levin *et al.*, 1989). This simple measure has been shown to correlate highly with an independent diagnosis of dementia. Over 30 per cent had scores of 3 or 4, consistent with a picture suggestive of moderate dementia and over 50 per cent had a score of 5 or 6, suggestive of severe dementia. Further support came from the comments of the carers themselves. Almost 60 per cent mentioned specifically that the person they cared for had a diagnosis of Alzheimer's disease or a related disorder. Others used phrases such as '[he is] really muddly. I forget what the doctor called it, it was a long name'.

Although many of the elderly people had problems such as dysphasia consistent with the impairments outlined above, there were still those in the sample who were able to talk in a moving way about their condition. A man, recently diagnosed as having Alzheimer's disease, made clear:

> *When this funny business comes over me, I get so tense and lost in a labyrinth. I feel like swearing hard at something but I don't know what.*

Physical health

The presence of physical problems could compound difficulties for the carer. Arthritis and heart disease were the most frequent problems in the elderly people, as reported by their carers. Over a third were said to have suffered cerebrovascular accidents. Smaller numbers were stated to have Parkinson's Disease.

Help with personal care

One of the most obvious ways in which the carers' daily lives were affected was in the amount of help with personal care they gave to the elderly people. We asked the carers about nine tasks in particular. These were: help with getting up, moving about, washing, dressing, bathing, using the lavatory, eating and drinking, taking medicines, and going out of the house.

Just under two-thirds of the elderly people required help with four or more of these activities. As one wife graphically said:

> *[It's] very hard work to be a full-time nurse at seventy years of age!*

In nearly all cases, this help was given by the carer alone. Thus, 92 per cent helped with at least one aspect of personal care (most frequently with taking medication and dressing). Only 12 per cent of carers had any help at all from another member of their family or a friend.

Sometimes there was a reluctance to involve people of the opposite gender in intimate personal care. A daughter in law, who lived with her husband and two teenage sons, bathed her mother in law on her own:

> *The biggest [problem] is bathing her because she is thirteen stone - it takes ages to do it.*

Twenty seven per cent of carers reported that services helped with these personal care routines but this was almost exclusively in the form of transport to day care, or less frequently, help with bathing.

Over 60 per cent of the elderly people could walk unaided and a further 21 per cent used a stick or a frame. Forty five per cent of the elderly people were incontinent, doubly so in almost half the cases. We were surprised that over 30 per cent of those carers looking after a person who was doubly incontinent had not been supplied with incontinence pads. Sometimes even pads were not enough. One husband stated that, because his wife would wander throughout the house, in an attempt to prevent further damage to the chairs, he had removed all the chair covers and wrapped bin liners around the seats before replacing them.

Other help from family and friends

Less than half the carers could remember an occasion when a friend or relative had taken over caring for them, even for a few hours. Sometimes this was through choice. A daughter in law and her husband said they had no relatives able to help and did not want assistance from their children, friends or neighbours - 'it's our responsibility'. Others commented that family and friends could not always be relied on. One daughter, separated from her husband, with two sons aged 11 and eight, caring for her 74 year old mother, said bitterly:

> They just don't appear....[my advice would be] you need to make sure you've got lots of people around that will turn up, not just say they will.

For carers who did receive support from family and friends, non-resident daughters were the prime source of help. However, nearly a quarter of all carers in the sample, whether married or single, had no children. Others pointed out that their family and friends were of a similar age group to themselves and so were unlikely to be ready to travel long distances to visit or to take on heavy physical tasks.

Time off from caring

Nearly everyone felt some degree of restriction through caring. 'I can't do much else,' said one wife, 'apart from look after him'. For example, half the carers were unwilling or felt it was unsafe to leave their relative alone in the house. Therefore, if they were to go out, it was imperative that there should be someone to take over the elderly person's care.

Over a third of carers felt that they spent too much time with the person cared for. Now, this clearly involves an element of perception. However, we also asked the carers to estimate the amount of time per week they spent apart from the elderly person, inclusive of *all* times when any person whatsoever took over the elderly person's care or when the carer left him or her alone. There was tremendous variation in the answers, ranging from no time at all to a maximum of 76 hours. The mean hours per week totalled 16 hours, with a median time per week of 12. It is important to recognise that the overwhelming proportion of time apart consisted of times when the elderly person was at day care or when sitters visited, a point which will become a recurring theme of later chapters.

As a point of comparison, albeit nothing other than tenuous, *Social Trends* (Central Statistical Office, 1993) suggests that retired people (the age group of most of the carers) can expect to spend 36 hours per week on essential domestic tasks, such as cooking, shopping, and personal care tasks, leaving them with around 80 hours per week free time and allowing for seven hours sleep a night. As we shall be emphasising, the carers had to use *their* time off to do essential household tasks and could by no means expect to have seven hours unbroken sleep.

Responses to caring

The remainder of this chapter will be taken up with a discussion of responses to caring and, in particular, upon outlining factors associated with an impact upon the carers' health. Most of our attention will revolve around scores on the General Health Questionnaire (GHQ) (Goldberg and Williams, 1988) and attitudes towards permanent residential care. These proved to be crucial influences upon outcome, as Chapter Eight will explain.

The carers' psychological health

The GHQ is a well validated self completion questionnaire. The version we used was the 28 item GHQ (GHQ28). It is not a diagnostic test but is designed to measure what is termed 'caseness'. This is taken to mean the likelihood that people with scores over a certain cut point are experiencing symptoms associated with depression, anxiety and hypochondriacal self-concern. In the version which we used, by coding each item as a dichotomous variable, this is taken to include all scores of between six and 28.

We also asked the carers to complete the SELFCARE (D) (Bird *et al.*, 1987). This 12 item questionnaire was designed as a screening test for depression in elderly people in primary care settings. With this measure, scores of between six and 12 are taken to be indicative of depression.

Forty per cent of the carers had GHQ scores of between six and 28. At 5.9, the mean score came just under the threshold for caseness. About 25 per cent of carers had scores suggestive of depression, as measured by SELFCARE (D). Here the mean score was 3.6. The correlation between SELFCARE (D) and the GHQ and its component subscales was, as was to be expected, very strong.

To summarise this information, 54 per cent of carers had scores below the threshold both for the GHQ and the SELFCARE (D). Nineteen per cent had raised scores on the GHQ only and seven per cent scored over the threshold for the SELFCARE (D)only. The remaining 20 per cent

scored above the threshold for the GHQ *and* the SELFCARE (D). This
picture was strengthened by our finding that just under ten per cent of
the carers were undergoing treatment with anxiolytics, antidepressants,
or antipsychotic medication.

What inferences can we draw from the carers' GHQ scores? The GHQ
has been used in a tremendous variety of settings, ranging from samples
of the general population to different occupational groups and people
with a wide range of physical health problems or psychiatric conditions.
The proportion of adults in community surveys who score as a case on
the GHQ tends to range mainly between 13 and 28 per cent, although
gender distributions and the GHQ version used may have some
influence (Bowling *et al.*, 1992). When consecutive attenders at general
practitioners' surgeries have been compared with random samples of the
same population, it has been shown that having a high GHQ score
makes it more likely that a person will consult their GP. Such studies of
primary care attenders have produced varying figures for the proportion
of those likely to score as a 'case' but two studies, the second a
replication of the first, produced a prevalence estimate of around 40 per
cent (Boardman, 1987). With respect to our sample, the results are
consistent with those other studies which have suggested that high GHQ
scores are to be found among resident carers of people with dementia,
and that the numbers of those scoring highly is greater than one might
have expected to find among the general population.

Given that one of the underpinning purposes behind the provision of
respite services is the intention to alleviate sources of stress for carers, it is
critical that we have very specific information upon this topic. What
factors did our analysis suggest were associated with raised GHQ scores?
The results are summarised in Table 2.2 and discussed in more detail
below.

The carers' age and health status

There was a very strong relationship between self-rated health status
and GHQ; those who had rated their health as poor were extremely
likely to have high GHQ scores. Interestingly, this remained true even
when we controlled for age and gender. In the same way, both men and
women who reported a longstanding illness or disability were likely to
have raised GHQ scores.

The characteristics of the elderly people

In keeping with a sample which largely consisted of people with
moderate or severe dementia, we found very strong associations
between the characteristics of those cared for and raised GHQ scores.
This did not centre around the amount of personal care required or
degree of cognitive impairment, although as we have seen both of these

were considerable, but around some of the behavioural characteristics of those cared for.

Table 2.2 Carers and their GHQ Scores

	% GHQ 0-5	% GHQ 6-28	Total (N)	Significance
Carer characteristics:				
Gender				
Man	72	28	*90*	chi-sqr 7.811
Woman	55	45	*197*	*p* = 0.0052
Self rated health				
Good	79	21	*97*	chi-sqr 42.436
Fairly good	63	37	*112*	*p* = 0.0000
Not good	31	69	*77*	
Time for leisure and hobbies				
No	46	54	*102*	chi-sqr 13.269
Yes	68	32	*182*	*p* = 0.0003
Characteristics of the elderly people:				
Mean BRS Score				
Mean score	15.68	18.39	*279*	F = 12.8075
(± 95% CL)	(± 0.97)	(± 1.12)		*p* = 0.0004
Mean trying behaviours score				
Mean score	4.17	5.29	*286*	F = 20.0154
(± 95% CL)	(± 0.32)	(± 0.37)		*p* = 0.0000
Total	**60**	**40**	***287***	

A *p* value of 0.05 means that the observed result has a 5% (1 in 20) probability of occurring by chance. A value of 0.01 means the observed result has a 1% (1 in 100) probability of occurring, and a *p* value of 0.001 means a probability 0.1%. The value *p* = 0.05 is conventionally used as the threshold of significance, with a value below 0.05 being considered significant. (In other words, the event is unlikely to have occurred by chance and therefore warrants an explanation.)

One important factor was if the carer was woken by the elderly person or had to accompany him or her to the lavatory during the night. Nearly half of the carers who reported that their sleep was interrupted at least twice a week (and more often every night) had high GHQ scores.

Carers looking after people who were more dependent had raised GHQ scores. This was true both in terms of overall dependency and on the mean and median scores on each subscale of the BRS, with the exception of the two questions dealing with communication. The subscale contributing most to GHQ scores was social disturbance (items 14-18) covering, for instance, wandering or interfering behaviour.

Similar results were obtained when we used the trying behaviours scale developed in previous work at NISW (Levin *et al.*, 1989). Treating each item discretely and as a summary total, there was an association between trying behaviours, such as being aggressive or abusive towards the carer, and high GHQ scores. By contrast, where the carer reported that the person cared for showed positive traits, such as being appreciative, it was probable that they had *lower* GHQ scores.

Restrictions on social contacts and leisure

Carers who reported that they lacked leisure time, felt lonely or had not seen family and friends often enough were particularly likely to have high GHQ scores. While it can be argued that it is hard to untangle which factors influenced which, we should not forget that these feelings do not only concern lack of contact with other family and friends but the sense of loss that could occur as a result of the elderly person's condition: 'I can't have a conversation with her, she's not like my mother any more'. Spouses were least likely to report that they lacked free time, suggesting that for other carers, it was particularly difficult to fit in their caring responsibilities with additional family or work commitments.

Gender and caring

Consistent with some of the studies described earlier, we found that women (especially wives and daughters) were more likely to have GHQ scores in the six to 28 range.

It was interesting that gender appeared to influence which factors appeared to contribute most to GHQ scores. As reported by their carers, neither the men nor women who were cared for were any more likely to be incontinent, to be more dependent as measured by the BRS or to have a greater number of trying behaviours. For *women* carers the factors in the elderly people most associated with high GHQ scores were, if the person they cared for were incontinent, and scored more highly on the physical disability, apathy and social disturbance subscales of the BRS. For men, only higher scores on the social disturbance subscales were associated with high GHQ scores. The association between GHQ scores and the reported number of trying behaviours was stronger for men than for women carers.

Temper loss

Another way in which we tried to get a sense of difficulties for the carers was to ask whether they had found themselves losing their temper. Over half the carers reported that they lost their temper sometimes and just over 20 per cent rated it as occurring often. The association between temper loss and GHQ scores was very strong.

Thirteen per cent of carers stated that they had definitely hit or shaken the person they cared for at some point. A wife described the triggering factors:

> *I've hit him a few times, he is such a handful. And at night when I've had to toilet him, and there's the relentless repeating of conversation.*

Others tried walking away or verbalising their anger:

> *My language can be strong at times! I'm not saying I haven't felt like it [hitting].*

Our information was, of course, dependent on self report but some strong associations emerged between hitting or shaking the person cared for and other factors. There was a particularly strong likelihood that the elderly person had attempted to hit the carer him or herself. Men were more likely to have been reported to have been hit by their carer than women. The association with temper loss was strong, suggesting that hitting the person cared for may have been a culmination of feelings of frustration. Carers who stated that they had definitely hit the person they cared for at some point were likely to be caring for someone who was incontinent, more cognitively impaired and dependent as measured by the CAPE, and to have stated that they felt lonely.

Length of time caring

One question which requires consideration is whether the length of time for which they had been caring had any effect. We asked the carers to estimate when they believed the person cared for had first shown problems associated with a diagnosis of Alzheimer's disease or a related disorder, such as an inability to remember recent events. While retrospective accounts are not to be compared with the accuracy of clinical examination, especially in cases of insidious onset where there is a clear possibility of underestimation, all we sought to establish was an approximate benchmark.

The mean length of time caring was almost five years. Less than 20 per cent had been caring for under a year. This was in keeping with the numbers with moderate or severe dementia among those cared for. As we described in Chapter One, the sample consisted of existing users of community services at a set point in time and ongoing new referrals. This second group were likely to have been caring for, on average, almost two years less. We found that these carers were more likely to have higher mean GHQ scores and to be caring for people less cognitively impaired and in need of help with personal care. This is in keeping with the assumption that the process of initiating services is often begun in response to indications of stress in the carer. It raises the possibility that, with time, carers may adjust to the changes taking place in the person for whom they care, but need support in developing ways of coping.

Attitudes to permanent residential care

Having outlined the difficulties faced by many of the carers in the sample, it was not surprising that over half the carers reported that they had felt unable to carry on at some time. A daughter in law made clear:

> There are some days when I feel I can't go on any longer and I feel murderous; some days I can cope perfectly well.

However, there was a vital distinction between feelings such as these and making the decision to cease caring. Just over 40 per cent of the carers said that someone, either another family member or professional, had suggested to them that they should consider arranging permanent residential care. Eighteen per cent had actually been given a concrete offer and, of these, less than half (n=13) were in the process of arranging an admission. So, while there was a degree of concordance between the carers' views and other people's, it is one of the most important findings of the study that just 11 per cent of the *whole* sample said that they would definitely agree to arranging residential care. Furthermore, over half said that it was something that they definitely could not countenance.

We shall be showing later just how crucial a determinant attitude to residential care was. For now, it is enough to discuss whether there were any factors which appeared to predict that a carer would be willing to consider ceasing to care. Spouses were particularly likely to say that they would definitely *not* choose residential care. Carers who scored highly on the GHQ and SELFCARE (D) and reported that they often found themselves losing their temper with the person they cared for were more likely to consider it, as were those caring for the most dependent elderly people. The carer's health status did *not* determine whether they were more likely to prefer this option, suggesting that, for many, a willingness to continue caring outweighed any health considerations of their own.

Closing issues and summary

Consistent with a sample comprising resident carers, most of whom were already in touch with community services, we found that nearly all of the people cared for showed evidence of moderate or severe dementia, and needed high degrees of support from their carers in terms of supervision and help with personal care.

The majority of carers were spouses and daughters of the people for whom they cared. In most cases, it was the carer alone who was undertaking the overwhelming proportion of caring responsibilities. The likelihood of age related health problems among the carers was strong; around 40 per cent reported a longstanding disability or illness of their own.

The homogeneity of the sample in terms of living arrangements, gender and age of the carers and those cared for, and type of tasks which the carers undertook was high. Within it, we were able to identify with some clarity many of the precise problems faced by the carers. We found that strong relationships existed between the characteristics of those cared for and the response of the carers. On the basis of the measures we used, some 40 per cent of the carers showed symptoms suggestive of non-psychotic psychiatric morbidity, such as depression or anxiety. Those whose health was poor and who were caring for dependent elderly people, particularly those who showed behavioural problems such as being abusive or aggressive, were especially likely to report these sorts of difficulties. This suggests that it is important for care managers, general practitioners and other professionals to be aware of the need to review carers' well-being regularly and take appropriate action at signs of difficulty.

Carers' needs for community care are not only dependent upon the needs of the person cared for but upon their own. On the evidence of the day-to-day routines of the carers whom we interviewed, we would suggest that the provision of respite services must be based upon three key elements. The first is the recognition of the unremitting nature of the type of help given by the carer. This meant that their opportunities for time off and leisure were limited to such times as when another person was available to assume the care of the elderly person. The second is an understanding that specific assistance may be required in helping the carer to deal with everyday difficulties, ranging from continence aids to specialised interventions for problem behaviours. The third is that responses to caring will vary. A recognition of individual needs, taking as much account as possible of personal preferences, is a prerequisite to arranging any package of respite services. It should also be acknowledged that, given that many carers have been caring for a person with a progressive illness for long periods, it is inevitable that their needs will change over time.

3   Assessment and Care Management

She [the social worker] knows what's available and can arrange things.

Background

We begin our examination of the services to the elderly people and their carers by focusing upon their contacts with general practitioners, psychogeriatricians, geriatricians, social workers and community psychiatric nurses. These professionals play an important part in the process whereby families gain access to practical help including respite services.

One of the key objectives of the community care reforms is to make proper assessment of need and good care management the cornerstone of high quality care. To this end, authorities have been provided with policy guidance and a series of practice guides on the process of care management and the options for implementing the changes (Department of Health 1990; 1991a, 1991b, 1991c, 1991d; SSI/SWSG, 1991a, and 1991b).

This guidance emphasises the importance of collaborative working between the various agencies, particularly where the needs of a client group or an individual are complex, and where it is difficult to make a distinction between health and social care. One such client group, on our evidence and that of others, is formed by elderly people with dementia and their carers: the complex set of medical, social and psychological needs which arise from dementia can rarely be met by one type of professional or one branch of the services.

Researchers and practitioners have drawn attention to the wide range of different systems of care management and different patterns of local services which existed before the final implementation of the new community care legislation in 1993 (Dant and Gearing, 1990; Lennon and Jolley, 1991; Lodge, 1991; Tym, 1991). The arrangements had in common the aim of providing multi-professional assessment and continuing support, and they involved, to varying degrees, joint action between agencies. Special schemes, too, have been initiated. For example, the Lewisham Care Management Scheme applies the pioneering University of Kent Personal Social Services Research Unit

[31]

model for the first time to elderly people with dementia, and other schemes involve care management systems based in general practice.

The study areas

The arrangements for assessment, long term care management and service delivery in our study areas provided examples of three very different approaches to the same tasks. As we shall show, each model had its own different implications for the elderly people and their carers, for the use of health and social services and hence for the base from which the new arrangements are being developed.

The variety in the assessment and care management systems found in the three study areas over the years 1989–1991 stemmed mainly from differences in the organisation of their psychogeriatric services. Each of the three areas had, and still has, community-oriented psychogeriatric services committed to extensive coverage of people with dementia, to multidisciplinary team work and to the support of carers. These services are well-established and have a reputation for pioneering sound, imaginative approaches. They differed, however, and continue to differ, in organisation, policy and practice, and in the quantity and mix of services which they could provide directly or negotiate from other agencies.

The service in Area One, a city in the south of England, was the most cohesive. The Unit was based in a hospital on a site which also housed the geriatric unit. The team attached priority to the provision of assessment, long term professional support and respite care to elderly people with dementia and the carers who lived with them. After assessment, elderly people living alone usually became the responsibility of social services. By contrast, those with resident carers were almost always allocated a community psychiatric nurse who visited regularly, co-ordinated packages of respite and reported back to the team at review meetings. The health service was a major supplier of respite in the form of continuing day hospital care, planned regular relief care in hospital, and a sitting service run by a voluntary organisation but closely integrated into the psychogeriatric service.

The service in Area Three, a city in the north, was based in a District General Hospital. The multi-disciplinary team was located in a separate building in which there was a day hospital and a small number of beds. The team and the day hospital concentrated upon thorough assessment. It provided only a small amount of relief care for people with severe dementia in two NHS special nursing home units. After assessment, most families were transferred to social workers based in area teams for long term care management. The service relied heavily upon close co-operation with social services for the provision of relief care in ordinary and specialist residential homes and with both social services and voluntary organisations for day care, sitting and carer support schemes.

By contrast, Area Two, which covered a town and villages in a Midlands county, had a community dementia team which was chaired and managed by a senior social worker and advised by a steering group. The team was based in premises close to the town centre where the consultant held a regular clinic and where day care was also provided. The members of the team provided assistance to elderly people living alone as well as to those living with their carers. The tasks of arranging and reviewing individual packages of care were undertaken by either a social worker or a community psychiatric nurse who had adopted a common approach. The consultant, the day hospital and NHS relief care facilities were located several miles away in a large psychiatric hospital. The team also devised packages of respite made up of social services and voluntary sector provision.

As can be seen, the differences lay mainly in the arrangements for long term care management after the joint assessment was completed. In Area One, the health service remained the lead agency for elderly people living with their carers, and the consultants and community psychiatric nurses offered NHS respite services and monitored and reviewed the home situation with the wider team up to and after an elderly person had died. This arrangement contrasted most sharply with the system in Area Three whereby, after assessment, social services usually became the lead agency, assigning the tasks of care management to social workers based in area teams and providing the bulk of practical services. The arrangement in Area Two occupied an intermediate position in which the community dementia team bridged the divide between health and social services, and both sectors provided practical services.

In addition, there were other differences within and between areas in the approaches of the various professionals to the complex processes of assessment and care management, especially when their practices were examined in detail. For example, the member of the multi-disciplinary team who made the first contact with the carers varied, the teams used an array of different assessment scales and forms, and the timing, content and pace of assessment differed, as did the informal negotiations with the families and other services which took place when arranging a package of care.

Despite this variety in the arrangements for care management, the general practitioners in each area were the main source of referrals to the specialist teams for diagnosis and comprehensive assessment. It is to them that families turn first when they notice changes in an elderly relative.

General practitioners

The great majority (95 per cent) of the elderly people and carers had seen their general practitioners about the health of the elderly person in the year before initial interview. Of this group, just over one-third last consulted their doctors in the previous four weeks, just under one-third last consulted more than one month but less than three months ago, and the rest last consulted over three months ago.

It was interesting that the proportion of elderly people in this sample who had seen their general practitioner in the last month was very similar to the proportion in the total elderly population, for in any one month about one in three persons aged 65 and over in Great Britain have seen their doctors (OPCS, 1990). Moreover, the likelihood that elderly people would have seen their doctors in the past three months did not vary by area or with the number of respite services used.

However, frequency of contact with general practitioners was very variable. Of those consulting their doctors in the previous year, just over one-third had seen them once or twice, just under one-third had seen them three or four times, and the rest had seen them more often. Many carers only contacted their doctors when they could not cope or when their relatives showed signs of acute illness; then they saw them several times in a few weeks. Others were given appointments at regular intervals. However, only one in eight elderly people had seen their doctors twelve or more times in the last year. The carers reported that these visits lasted, on average, a quarter of an hour. Three in four elderly people were usually seen in their own homes rather than at the surgery.

The carers' views

Although contact with family doctors was variable and often episodic, 88 per cent of the carers regarded their doctors as helpful, a proportion which included 49 per cent who regarded them as very helpful.

The carers described a wide range of benefits accruing from their doctors' intervention. Almost all the carers mentioned the expert help given in the form of investigation, diagnoses and treatment of their relatives' often multiple health problems. Mrs Smale said:

> *He's done more than anyone else with the tablets.*

Over and above direct medical intervention, many carers commented on other benefits which timely attention from their doctors had brought them. Referral on to consultants was mentioned by over half the carers, and referral to other services, such as community nursing and home help, was mentioned by about one quarter of them. Mrs Coker, who had seen the family doctor four times in the previous year, described her as very helpful:

> *She put me in touch with (the psychogeriatric unit), she prescribed me antidepressants .... gave mother a complete physical examination. I feel she's interested.*

Referrals made by doctors to other services were particularly appreciated because they often led to the provision of regular practical help. For example, Mr Scott, who was looking after his wife, regarded his doctor as helpful because:

He put us on to the meals on wheels and Dr (the psychogeriatrician).

Mrs Thrower, who was looking after her husband, commented:

She's a very good doctor. If it hadn't been for her, I wouldn't have got the help I've got.

The carers gave high praise to general practitioners who saw their patients regularly, showed concern for their own well-being as well as that of their relatives, and provided advice and encouragement. Such activity on the part of family doctors was mentioned by about two in five carers. 'He's a terrific support, fantastic', said Mrs Gower, whose doctor visited every two months and had referred her husband to both the psychogeriatrician and geriatrician, resulting in regular visits from a community psychiatric nurse and day care twice a week.

This type of continuing back-up and review was the sort of help which would have been valued by some of the carers who expressed dissatisfaction with the service from their doctors. Mrs Charles said:

He doesn't come to see her, I asked him to come and he took her blood pressure and said she looks all right.

In addition, a few carers were of the opinion that their doctor had been reluctant to refer them on to specialists or had referred them on too late so that they went without help potentially available to them.

Issues

Research has shown that general practitioners vary widely in their capacity and commitment to identifying dementing patients and that, even when a diagnosis of severe dementia is made, they may not refer on to specialist services (Iliffe *et al.*, 1990; O'Connor *et al.*, 1988; Philp and Young, 1988). The availability of simple screening devices, and the requirements under the new general practitioner contract to offer an assessment annually to patients aged 75 and over, to refer on patients to specialist services and to provide advice on social services, afford an opportunity to improve practice in this area and to improve identification rates.

As we have shown, the carers in this study were coping with chronically ill elderly people, many of whom were severely cognitively impaired and had multiple health problems. They valued doctors who provided active medical treatment, who monitored their patient's progress, provided advice and encouragement and referred them on for specialist and practical services which they themselves could not provide. It is essential that general practitioners have easy access to these services and up to date information about the sources and kinds of help potentially available to patients with dementia and their carers in their locality. On our evidence, general practitioners are key to forging links with relevant services. Indeed, most families in the study had gained access to practical help and professional support as a result of referrals by their own doctors for assessment and advice from the specialist services.

Psychogeriatricians and geriatricians

The great majority (83 per cent) of elderly people in this sample had been assessed by consultants specialising in the care of older people. Overall, 75 per cent of carers knew that their elderly relative had been seen by psychogeriatricians and 18 per cent knew that he or she had been seen by geriatricians, proportions which include the 10 per cent of elderly people seen by both.

In Area One, where the service was renowned for its extensive coverage of people with dementia in the community, the proportion of elderly people seen by psychogeriatricians was, at 84 per cent, higher than in the other two areas, where in both cases it was 71 per cent. There was also some variation in contact with geriatricians between areas, with elderly people in Area Three being most likely to have seen them and those in Area Two least likely to have done so.

Geriatric and psychogeriatric services often work closely together referring to each other, especially when patients have dementia combined with other significant physical illnesses and disabilities. Given the arrangements for people with dementia in the study areas, and the comparatively limited practical help that geriatric services could provide on completion of investigation, diagnoses and treatment, it was not surprising that more elderly people had seen psychogeriatricians.

As expected, the elderly people without respite services and those with one or more of them were equally likely to have seen consultants. However, the length of time elapsing since the carers and, so far as they knew, the people for whom they cared had seen consultants increased with the number of respite services allocated. For example, of the families assessed by psychogeriatricians, almost three-quarters of those without respite services had last talked to their consultants less than three months ago, as against only a third of those with all three respite services.

Many of those without respite services had only recently been referred for assessment or were reviewed quarterly, which in part explains their more recent contact. By contrast, some of those with respite services were monitored by other professionals in the team. In addition, the carers may have overestimated the time elapsing since the elderly people had last seen the consultants because they were not told of examinations at the day hospital or on relief care wards and recalled only the last time they themselves had seen the consultant.

The carers' views

The majority of carers who had contact with either type of specialism felt that it had been beneficial: overall, 78 per cent of these carers regarded the psychogeriatricians as helpful, and 67 per cent regarded the geriatricians as helpful. As in the case of general practitioners, the carers emphasised both the consultants' professional skills and the regular support that the services provided or offered as a result of their assessments.

Firstly, most of these carers mentioned approvingly that the consultants listened to them, showed understanding of their problems, and provided them with clear explanations and advice. Mrs Silver, who found the psychiatrist a lot of help with her husband, said:

> *He'll explain anything to me I ask him.*

Secondly, the carers were positive about the specialists for examining their relatives regularly, diagnosing treatable conditions or referring on to other consultants or other experts, such as continence advisers. Miss Bolt said:

> *He has been helpful, he noticed she was having some trouble with her thyroid glands and sorted that out.*

Thirdly, the carers were often appreciative of assessment by the specialist team because it resulted in practical help. Mrs Hanson, a daughter, commented:

> *It opens up the doors to more day care - you seem to be able to get more services if you're diagnosed 'psychogeriatric'.*

It was the practice of the psychiatrists in one area to visit all families newly referred to them at home and often to continue to visit at regular intervals. This individual attention was welcomed by the carers and appeared to inspire confidence. 'He's like granite, such a strength', said one carer with experience of domiciliary visits. Another carer apparently agreed:

> *He's very nice. I don't know how much help he'll be but I hope he keeps coming. He's organising day care.*

Opinions were divided on the value of regular review, especially at out-patient clinics: some carers liked their situation to be monitored and to be reminded of services available or offered more of them; others found the journey to the clinic taxing or could not see the point of the exercise. A husband said:

He just asks us how she's been and that's it.

A minority of carers had not found their contact with the specialist services helpful or could not identify lasting benefits. A few of these had been disappointed that, 'He can't make her better'. The worst fears of one carer had been confirmed when the consultant had explained the diagnosis but had admitted that, other than support, there was nothing he could offer. Most carers, however, found the support offered by the services after their family doctors had referred them to the specialist teams very beneficial. Mrs Neal summed up the value of her contact with the psychogeriatrician:

Without getting in touch with him, I wouldn't have had any help at all.

Issues

We noted that many but not all the carers knew the name of their consultant and how to contact a social worker or community psychiatric nurse in the multi-disciplinary team. However, only a minority seemed well informed about the complex process of assessment and care management. Firstly, some carers did not appear to know how the team worked once a referral had been received, who participated in the assessments or how the decision was reached to offer a particular package of care. Secondly, some did not realise that a consultant, social worker or community psychiatric nurse may have visited them on behalf of all the team. Thirdly, one team invited the carers and elderly people to the meeting at which the results of the assessment and the care plans for the future were discussed but this practice was uncommon. We suggest, therefore, that each multi-disciplinary team should check whether they are giving the carers clear information about their procedures and involving them closely in every stage of the assessment and re-assessment process.

In this branch of the services, as in all the others, there was room to review working methods. Nevertheless, many carers had benefited greatly from careful assessment by the consultants and their colleagues, obtaining practical services and professional support. Timely referral to these services seemed crucial.

Social workers and community psychiatric nurses

Although social workers and community psychiatric nurses are members of different professions and are employed by different sectors of the services, there are good reasons for examining their roles in tandem.

First, there were common and overlapping elements in the work of these practitioners in the study areas. Thus both sets of professionals made home visits for the purpose of assessment, review and the provision of continuing support; both designed and co-ordinated packages of services, referring to each other and various agencies for services their own did not provide; both worked together in multi-disciplinary teams, and both were heavily involved in the process whereby respite care services were allocated to and rationed among families.

Second, we shall show that there were differences between the study areas in the likelihood that a social worker or a community psychiatric nurse would become the professional most closely involved with a family on a long term basis.

Third, now that social services have become the lead agency for assessment and care management arrangements, there is a lot of interest in the degree of overlap and specialism in the activities of social workers and community psychiatric nurses, for both may be allocated the role of key professional worker under the new system.

Contact

Overall, 67 per cent of the carers and 52 per cent of the elderly people had talked to social workers before our first interview, and 37 per cent of the carers and elderly people had been visited by community psychiatric nurses. If the arrangements for service delivery in the three areas are to be understood, we have to look at the enormous and inter-linked variation between areas in contact with these professionals. Given our knowledge of the local services, it was unsurprising to find that the carers in Area One were far less likely to have talked to social workers than those in Area Two or Area Three (40 per cent versus 73 per cent and 93 per cent). The variation between areas in the use of community psychiatric nursing services was even more marked. Seventy per cent of the carers in Area One, compared with 35 per cent of those in Area Two and only four per cent of those in Area Three were visited by community psychiatric nurses.

Half of the carers involved with social workers had talked to them in the last four weeks, a proportion which rose to two-thirds if the time were extended to three months. As in the case of doctors, frequency of contact was variable: some carers talked to their social workers regularly about their care arrangements and others contacted them for specific advice. Whilst about one-third of those seen by social workers had

talked to them at least twelve times in the previous year, at the other end
of the continuum, about one-third had talked to them only once or twice.

Some of this contact took place over the telephone, but most carers
were also visited at home. Social workers' visits lasted, on average,
about 40 minutes, with visits of about 30 minutes being the most
frequently reported, and visits of about one hour the next most
frequently reported. The timing and intensity of contact with social
workers appeared to depend partly on the practice of individual social
workers and partly on the task upon which they were engaged with the
family. For example, transitions to day care or residential care involved
more contact than monitoring a well-established service package.

Community psychiatric nurses generally operated a system of regular
review visiting. Over one-third of the carers they assisted were usually
visited at least fortnightly, a proportion which rose to two-thirds visited
at least once a month. There were different reasons for very frequent
visits: some nurses visited newly referred families very often in order to
build up a good working relationship, some were visiting regularly to
administer and monitor medication, and others were doing so because a
carer was at breaking point and residential care for the elderly person
was imminent.

The carers' views

The great majority of carers visited by social workers or community
psychiatric nurses were positive about the assistance given. Of those
allocated community psychiatric nurses, 44 per cent indicated that their
visits had made a lot of difference to their lives and a further 40 per cent
indicated that it had made some difference. Very similar proportions of
carers with social workers considered their involvement to be either a lot
of help or some help to them.

What then were these professionals doing with and for the carers and
elderly people which was so widely appreciated? Of course, there were
some forms of help which community psychiatric nurses could provide
directly but social workers could not, and vice versa. For example, the
nurse could give medication prescribed by doctors, and the social
workers could arrange social services day care without making a referral
to another agency. Nonetheless, there was a common core of activities in
which both professionals were engaged. As in the case of doctors, these
activities often brought lasting benefits to carers.

At a general level, both social workers and community psychiatric
nurses were valued for providing a single point of contact with the range
of services potentially relevant to their problems. The carers often
commented that they found it useful to have the name and telephone
number of one professional who would respond promptly to requests for
advice. For example, Miss Allen said of the psychiatric nursing service:

It helps one - gives me confidence that someone is there if I need them.

Similarly, Mr Ayres said of his social worker:

She's there if I need her, she's very attentive and she 'phones to make sure everything is okay.

Some carers found it therapeutic to have a professional who understood what it was like to live with a person with dementia, who listened to them and counselled them. Mrs Bowes said of her social worker:

I can talk to her. I tell her things I wouldn't tell our family.

This carer gave as an example her wish that her husband would die from another cause rather than gradually get worse through Alzheimer's disease. Other carers, however, did not feel the need for 'someone to talk to', preferring to contact the services only when in difficulty.

Many carers particularly valued the practitioners' knowledge of services and benefits, and of how to go about getting them. Thus half the carers visited by community psychiatric nurses mentioned that they had arranged practical services, whereas only one quarter mentioned their help with medication. Of those who had talked to social workers, about 70 per cent mentioned that they had arranged respite services and 40 per cent mentioned that they had arranged other services. For example, Mrs Lurie explained:

She told us all about help with money, helped filling the forms out, and took us to the day centre for the first time.

The carers' replies to questions about whether anyone had given them information about the services available and whether anyone from the services was taking a special interest in their care arrangements confirmed that social workers and community psychiatric nurses undertook key tasks in service delivery.

Firstly, half of the carers said that someone had told them about the range of services available to help people in their position. Social workers and nurses stood out as the main suppliers of information, with doctors or more than one professional said to undertake the task by small minorities of the carers.

Secondly, only 43 per cent of the carers said that someone from the services had told them that they would be taking a special interest in the arrangements made to help them. Almost all this group named social workers or community psychiatric nurses.

In a sample of carers identified by the arrangers and providers of respite care, the finding that half the carers could not recall being told about the services available suggested scope for improvements in practice, as did the finding that 57 per cent of the carers could not recall being told that a professional was taking a special interest in their care arrangements.

We asked the interviewers whether they felt that there was a professional who appeared to have overall responsibility for planning and arranging the package of care received by the carer and elderly person. In seven in ten cases, the interviewers were able to identify such a person, most usually a community psychiatric nurse or social worker.

Despite our efforts to avoid jargon, and thus reduce the potential for under-reporting, when we asked the carers a similar question, only four in ten said that there was one person who co-ordinated services. Once more, it was usually a community psychiatric nurse or social worker.

Issues

In 1992, local authorities had to prepare their first community care plans which set out information for individual users and carers about community care services and the arrangements they would be making for care management. For the future, we suggest that some of the following results from the study will have continuing relevance.

The first point is that health service professionals have an important contribution to make throughout all the stages of care management. The carers placed a high value on the advice given by general practitioners, psychogeriatricians, geriatricians and community psychiatric nurses and on the part they played in arranging and planning services for them. This means that community care plans must continue to be developed jointly and have the flexibility to take account of the varying and changing needs of this client group.

Next, the carers in our sample were nearly always reliant upon the information given to them by social workers, general practitioners and other professionals. This varied considerably both in its form and quality, or indeed whether it was given at all. It is essential that professionals have up to date knowledge and details about services, and that this is shared with the elderly people and carers with whom they are working.

It was clear that carers did not always know the name, profession, or telephone number of the professional who had contacted them. Therefore, our third suggestion is that, once a carer has been allocated a care manager, it is essential that he or she should know who this person is and what they can expect of them. Similarly, the care manager should give thorough explanations of the assessment procedures, the reasons behind any other professional's involvement and how each service will work together. The carers and those for whom they care should also be given some idea of the time scale for involvement by services and what other options might be available in the future.

Self-evident as some of these points may seem, it is attention to these sorts of details that will ensure that the high quality of the service provided to some of those in our sample becomes as widely available as possible.

Conclusion

Our findings confirm that general practitioners, consultants, social workers and community psychiatric nurses occupy the front line position in service delivery. Although these professionals each have unique skills, there are common and overlapping elements in their work. These include making assessments and re-assessments, making referrals, providing direct services such as information, advice and counselling, playing a part in the process of allocating services, and monitoring and changing packages of care.

These practitioners work for different authorities or different sectors of the same services. It is a complex task to co-ordinate all their efforts so that a wide range of individual needs can be met. It is essential that they have the structures, training and commitment to work together, and that they are able to offer the carers a range of high quality practical services. In the next chapter we shall show that the respite services that they offer are purchased and provided by different sectors of the services, that two or three forms of respite are often required, and that they form part of a wider package of care. We will also provide more evidence of the heavy involvement of health and social services professionals in the processes of arranging, monitoring and developing respite services.

We have highlighted the considerable skills required to make thorough, sensitive assessments and to construct long term packages of care which are appropriate, acceptable and flexible. In a new programme of research, we shall be investigating the processes of assessment and care management in greater detail and we shall be examining the roles and tasks of social workers under the new arrangements for community care.

4   Types and Mixes of Respite

This carer has excellent support from relief breaks, day hospital, community psychiatric nurse and the sitting service.

She has no relief breaks and doesn't want them.

(Interviewers)

Introduction

Our study set out to establish the characteristics of elderly people and their carers who used either day care or sitting or relief care services, or a combination of them. It provides new information about the users of different packages of respite, thereby contributing to the pool of knowledge on patterns of service allocation.

We shall begin by describing the number, type and mix of respite services which were used by the carers in our sample. Next, we shall consider the targeting of these services on different groups of carers and on elderly people with particular sets of problems. We shall go on to give examples of the context in which the carers found the various packages useful to them. Finally, we shall describe the other community services which the carers and elderly people had obtained.

In this chapter we aim to provide a background to the next three chapters in which we consider each type of respite separately and to introduce some of the questions we shall tackle when we look at the outcomes for the elderly people and their carers in our penultimate chapter.

Number of respite services

Figure 4.1 shows that we achieved the required variation in the number of respite services which the carers used. Of the total sample, 44 carers were not using day, sitting or relief care; the number with one, two or three services was 81, 122 and 40 respectively.

Figure 4.1 shows also that more than half the carers in this sample had a package of respite made up of two or three services, and that they were most likely to have two types of service. Many of the elderly people required as much help and supervision as elderly people in residential care and they received much more help from their carers than from anyone else. This raises many questions about respite services. For example, how much of a break from caring was typically obtained by using a combination of respite services? Did the respite services meet the carers' requirements for a break? Would the carers have liked a longer break? We shall provide some answers to these questions in later chapters.

Figure 4.1 Number of Respite Services

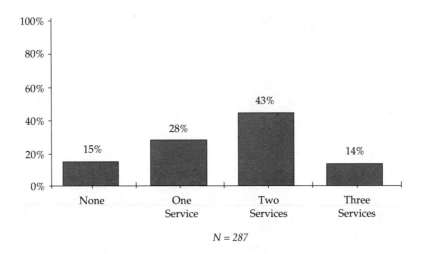

$N = 287$

The number of respite services allocated to the carers varied between the areas. We knew from preparatory work that there were differences between the areas in the amounts and sources of respite for the carers of elderly people with dementia and also in professional practice at the point of assessment. As we had expected, these differences were reflected in the sample. There were two main contrasts.

First, about 20 per cent of the carers in Area One and in Area Two were not using respite services, compared with only four per cent of the carers in Area Three. This difference arose in part because elderly people in Area Three were more likely to be assessed in a day hospital; in addition, this area had more facilities for continuing day care, as we shall see in Chapter Five.

Second, the carers in Area One were more likely to use three respite services than those in the other two areas (22 per cent versus eight per cent and 11 per cent). This reflected the wider availability of sitting services and their use to supplement the relatively limited day care available in Area One. Despite such variety, it was striking that the majority of carers who were using respite services in each area had a package of two or three services (Area One: 68 per cent; Area Two: 72 per cent; Area Three: 61 per cent).

Furthermore, the elderly people and carers with two respite services, and those with three of them were very similar in terms of their characteristics. Therefore, in our analyses, we have grouped them together.

The predominance of packages of respite was confirmed when we looked at how many of the carers and elderly people with a particular service were also using another form of respite. Over three-quarters of those with day care and, similarly, over three-quarters of those with sitting were using another respite service; of those with relief care, almost 90 per cent used day care, sitting or both of them.

Types of respite

Table 4.1 complements Figure 4.1 by identifying the types of respite which had been obtained by the carers with one, two or three services. The following points are particularly important and recur throughout the book.

Table 4.1 Number and Types of Respite

	Type of service	Carers with service	
		%	N
One	Day care only	18	44
	Sitting only	7	17
	Relief care only	8	20
Two	Day care and sitting	6	15
	Day and relief care	39	94
	Sitting and relief care	5	13
Three	Sitting, day and relief care	17	40
	Total	**100**	**243**

Firstly, two-thirds of these carers were using more than one respite service. Therefore, when evaluating a single respite service, it is necessary to take account of the wider package. Secondly, most carers had day care and most had relief care; by comparison, only a minority had sitting services.

A third and inter-related point was that there were many more carers with a package of day and relief care than there were with any other type of respite. A package which included day and relief care was used by 56 per cent of those with respite services. Even though there were differences between areas in the number and types of respite allocated, in each area the carers were more likely to have day or relief care than sitting services, and in each area they were most likely to have a package made up of day and relief care.

The predominance of the day and relief care package might be expected. Both day and relief care are provided by health and social services, and by the voluntary and private sectors; by contrast, sitting services are only patchily available and their level of provision is lower. However, the frequent use of this package has implications for the purchasers and providers of services and, above all, for the elderly people and their carers. We think that it raises a number of questions which merit debate, further research and experimentation.

One question is whether the package of day and relief care is widely used because it is the preferred option of many carers, or because sitting services are in short supply. We shall show later that most carers had either been allocated or offered day care and, subsequently, relief care; however, only a minority of carers had been allocated or offered sitting services. In addition, we shall show that some carers, especially husbands and wives were reluctant to use relief care and accepted it only when they were at breaking point.

A second question relates to the effects of the day and relief care packages on the elderly people, especially those who have to leave home for two in every eight weeks. In Chapter Seven, we shall discuss the carers' opinions on their relatives' experience of relief care, showing that these were more divided and less likely to be positive than they were in the case of day care and sitting.

Against this background, a further question is whether the use of relief care outside the home would be reduced by easily obtainable domiciliary and day care services which span 24 hours a day, every day of the week and every week of the year? This question cannot be answered without developments in services, creative care packaging, and research with a random allocation or other comparative design.

Our last questions are concerned with the costs and the management of packages of day and relief care: how can the provision of this package to many carers be orchestrated so that both the needs of individual carers are met sensitively and resources are used efficiently? Do costings of this package take account of the practice of keeping the day care place free while an elderly person is at relief care?

Again, these are important issues which arise from our study but which we did not set out to answer. New studies, which take stock of existing practice and identify the strengths and weaknesses of different approaches, would seem to be required. Such work would have to take account of the target group for this package, the characteristics of which we discuss in the next section.

Allocation of respite care

Our previous work showed, and more recent studies have confirmed that, compared with others, elderly people with dementia make heavy use of a multiplicity of community services, and are more likely to enter residential care (Levin *et al.*, 1989; O'Connor *et al.*, 1989; Livingston *et al.*, 1990; Cullen *et al.*, 1992). In the first NISW sample, which included elderly people living alone, we found that day and relief care were particularly likely to be allocated to those who lived with their carers and were, on several measures, more disabled than others. This study concentrated on a more dependent group. We asked ourselves whether it would yield any evidence that respite services were targeted, in line with the objective of official policy, 'on those in greatest need'.

The elderly people

When interpreting our findings on the targeting of services within this sample it must be remembered that the great majority of elderly people showed signs of marked or severe dementia. Table 4.2 sets out a selection of our evidence which showed that there were strong links between, on the one hand, the characteristics of the elderly people and, on the other hand, the number of respite services used.

Table 4.2 Characteristics of the Elderly People by the Number of Respite Services

	Number of Respite Services				
	% None	% One	% 2 - 3	Total (N)	Significance
Elderly people					
Household					
Live with carer only	18	32	50	206	chi-sqr 12.86
Live with carer and other	7	20	73	81	p = 0.002
Continent					
Yes	23	31	46	160	chi-sqr 21.05
No	6	24	70	76	p = 0.000
Normal conversation					
Yes	27	31	42	95	chi-sqr 19.94
No	9	27	64	191	p = 0.000
Information and orientation score					
None, mild, moderate (6-12)	20	32	48	112	chi-sqr 8.15
Marked (3-5)	17	25	58	78	p = 0.086
Severe (0-2)	7	25	68	68	
Mean	6.3	5.9	4.6	5.2	t value 2.85
					p = 0.005
CAPE BRS score					
Independent, low, medium dependency (0-12)	35	35	30	72	chi-sqr 46.31 p = 0.000
High (13-17)	17	32	51	76	
Maximum (18+)	4	24	72	131	
Mean	11.5	15.4	18.9	16.8	t value -7.68
					p = 0.000
Total sample	**15**	**28**	**57**	**287**	

First, Table 4.2 shows that elderly people who lived only with their carers were less likely to have respite services than those living with their carers and other relatives. In addition, elderly people living only with their carers were less likely to use two or three respite services than those in larger households.

Next, Table 4.2 shows that the precise problems of the elderly people were associated with the number of services used. Compared to elderly people who were continent, those who were incontinent were far more likely to use respite services and to have two or three of them. A similar contrast emerged when we compared elderly people who could converse normally with those who could not.

Of course, incontinence and an inability to converse normally are particular problems associated with a diagnosis of dementia. As might be expected, therefore, the elderly person's score on the Information and Orientation Test of the CAPE was associated with their use of respite services. Table 4.2 shows that the mean score of those with two or three services was lower, suggesting greater cognitive impairment, than the mean scores of the other two groups.

The Behaviour Rating Scale (BRS) of the CAPE covers all the problems we have discussed and is a useful means of summarising the evidence on the targeting of services. Table 4.2 shows a strong association between level of dependency and the use of services. The mean BRS score increased sharply in line with the number of services used. At 15.4, the mean BRS score of those using only one service was within the high dependency category; at 19, the score of those using two or three services was within the maximum dependency category. Research in York concluded that those whose BRS scores were greater than 13:

> are likely to need residential care .... supporting such people at home is likely to be very costly or a very heavy burden if they live with their relatives.
>
> (Pattie and Heaton, 1990)

The results of our preliminary analysis alerted us to similar questions. For example, was the level of dependency in the elderly people a major predictor of whether they remained at home, entered residential care or died in the subsequent year? Did the use of a package of respite affect these outcomes? We shall try to answer these questions in Chapter Eight.

Other findings, which are not shown in Table 4.2, confirmed that the majority of the elderly people without respite services were younger and more able than the others, and that the use of respite services increased in line with increasing levels of dependency in the elderly people. Elderly people without respite services were a younger group than those with two or three types of respite. The mean age rose from 77.4 for those without services, to 78.4 for those with one service, and to 79.9 for those with two or three services ($p = 0.05$). The number of respite services used also increased with the need for help with personal care and with the degree of behavioural disturbance. For example, the proportion of elderly people needing help with four to nine personal care routines rose from 33 per cent of those without respite, to 69 per cent of those with a single respite service, and to 82 per cent of those with two or three services. In addition, the proportion of elderly people with a high number of major behavioural and interpersonal problems rose from 16 per cent of those without respite, to 35 per cent of those with one service, and to 48 per cent of those with two or three services.

In broad terms, our findings show that the contrast between those without respite and those with a package of respite was most marked, and that those with a single respite service occupied the intermediate position. Nevertheless, it is only in the context of this sample that elderly people who were not using respite services appeared less dependent: their mean score on the BRS (11.5) alone suggested that they required a substantial amount of help and supervision.

The carers

The characteristics of the carers varied with the number of respite services which they used even when we allowed for their association with the characteristics of the elderly people.

First, Table 4.3 shows that wives and husbands, and, hence, the oldest group of carers, were least likely to use respite services; in addition, compared with younger carers, many of whom were daughters, they were less likely to use two or three services.

Table 4.3 shows also that the mean GHQ score of the carers with two or three types of respite was higher than the mean score of those with one type of respite, and of those receiving no respite care. The finding that about half of the carers with two or three types of respite had a high number of symptoms of depression and anxiety (GHQ score of six and over) was a cause for concern, especially as the majority of carers with this package of respite were looking after severely dependent elderly people. Again, the results of our preliminary analyses raised some important questions. For example, did the services react to high levels of emotional distress in a carer by offering a relatively intensive package of respite? Or were they unable to prevent emotional distress as an elderly person's abilities deteriorated? Were the respite services being used to substitute for residential care when the strains of caring were becoming intolerable?

A partial answer to the last question was provided by our findings on the strong association between the carers' attitude towards permanent residential care and the number of respite services they had been allocated, as shown in Table 4.3. At the first interview, the great majority

(82 per cent) of those who said that they would accept residential care
for the elderly person, if they were offered it, were already using two or
three types of respite; by contrast, about half of those who would not
have accepted residential care used two or three types of respite. In
Chapter Eight, we shall assess the extent to which a carer's willingness to
accept residential care affected what happened to an elderly person in
the subsequent year.

Table 4.3 Characteristics of the Carers by the Number of Respite Services

| | Number of Respite Services | | | | |
	% None	% One	% 2 - 3	Total (N)	Significance
Carers					
Relationship to elderly person					
Wife/husband	22	32	46	166	chi-sqr 24.21
Daughter, son, in law	10	18	79	62	p = 0.000
Other	10	27	63	59	
Mean Age	72.8	68.4	63.7	66.4	
GHQ score					
GHQ 0-5	17	33	50	173	chi-sqr 8.09
GHQ 6-28	12	21	67	114	p = 0.017
Mean	4.9	4.2	6.9	5.9	
Would accept residential care					
Yes	3	15	82	62	chi-sqr 20.32
No	18	31	51	215	p = 0.000
Number of hours apart from elderly person each week					
0-8	38	33	29	97	chi-sqr 74.86
9-17	1	31	68	76	p = 0.000
18+	5	22	73	97	
Mean	7.2	14.8	19.3	16.2	
Total sample	15	28	57	287	

Finally, Table 4.3 shows the strong influence of the provision of
respite on the number of hours which an elderly person and their carer
spent apart from each other in a typical week. One consequence of not
receiving respite services was that the carers and their relatives were
apart from each other, on average, only seven hours in a week,
compared with an average of 15 hours for those with one type of respite,

and an average of 19 hours for those with two or three types of respite. The carers estimated the total number of hours that they were apart from their relatives; except for the small minority in paid employment, the number of hours apart depended mainly upon whether a carer had respite services, a finding which highlighted the importance of these services to the carers in this sample.

Clearly, it was encouraging that respite services doubled the number of hours that, on average, a carer and an elderly person had a break from each other's company; on the other hand, we were not surprised that the carers with two or three types of respite reported greater degrees of restriction: after all, most looked after a relative who needed help with many aspects of personal care, half had a break of less than 19 hours a week when this relative was at home, and half showed signs of great psychological strain.

Researchers, health and social services professionals and carers' organisations have suggested that respite services alone may not prevent anxiety or depression in a carer or the admission of an elderly person into residential care once a carer is predisposed to accept this alternative. This viewpoint cannot be supported or refuted without studies which follow up the families over a period of time. The results of our follow up study may fuel the debate, and are reported in Chapter Eight.

Under the next headings we use the quantitative data from the first interviews with the carers to provide a fuller picture of the carers without any respite services, those with one type of respite and those with two or three types of respite.

The carers without respite

Fifteen per cent of the carers in the sample did not use any respite services. Some of these had been referred to service providers only recently. Others had refused respite as unnecessary, but kept in touch with a social worker or community psychiatric nurse or had support from their relatives. Some were reluctant to accept help of any kind or cared for a person who refused respite care.

Mr and Mrs Marks were a couple who had been referred to the psychogeriatrician only one month before the initial interview. Mrs Marks, aged 83, was partially sighted, showed signs of moderate cognitive impairment and was highly dependent on her husband, aged 87. Mr Marks said:

I feel pleased to be able to look after her .... I can't go out without her but I'm settled to it.

This couple were never apart. They had seen their general practitioner, whom he described as good, twice in the past year. Mr Marks had refused the home help service because:

I've got to have something to do. I enjoy cooking. I do the washing myself.

However, tension in the household was beginning to build up:

Her health has made her cantankerous and she keeps asking questions all the time.

Mr Marks would not accept a sitting service because 'my wife wouldn't like it and so I wouldn't like it'. The psychogeriatrician's suggestion that Mrs Marks should attend the day hospital once a week had met with agreement and her husband was, as he put it, 'waiting for instructions'. His reasons for acceptance in the first instance were interesting:

They would find out if there's something in the mind that's out of balance. I'd like to know that her mind won't get worse.

On follow up, Mrs Marks had been going to day care for a year, and had had one episode of relief care; the home help service had been accepted and a community psychiatric nurse was visiting regularly.

Mr and Mrs Avon had refused respite services as unnecessary. They had a very supportive family, a general practitioner who visited very often and back up from the community dementia team. Mr Avon had Alzheimer's disease and heart disease. His wife could not leave him alone but she had no difficulty in getting out because a son lived with them, and a daughter and other relatives made frequent visits. Mrs Avon found the consultant who examined her husband once every three months helpful. She also found the social worker who visited at least once in every three months very helpful in arranging for bathing aids, providing the forms to claim the attendance allowance and offering day care. Mr Avon had started to go to day care once a week three months before the first interview but he had stopped going after four weeks. He disliked day care:

I did not relax because I was too worried about him.

Although a sitting service was not required because, 'we have plenty of family', she said of relief care:

I am thinking about it. I might be able to have a holiday.

Other elderly couples lacked the unusually intensive support given to Mrs Avon by her family but they were able to manage with assistance from home helps and bath nurses weekly.

Although elderly people without respite services were the least dependent group in this sample, a minority of them were severely dependent. Some of their carers were reluctant to have help; others did not have help because their relative had refused it.

Mrs Main, aged over 90, lived with both her children. Her previously dominant role in the family had shaped the way they had adapted to caring, dovetailing their hours of work and social life so that their mother was never left alone longer than three hours. When her daughter was asked if she would like a particular service, she responded:

The crux of that question is if she'd accept it.

Mrs Main had attended the day hospital for assessment but would not accept continuing day care in a social services centre. Her daughter had refused relief care but commented:

If she wanted to go, it would be nice for us to have a fortnight on our own.

The reluctance of an elderly person, a carer or both to accept help sometimes posed a greater threat to survival at home than was the case with Mrs Main. Two very elderly sisters, living in straightened circumstances, were determined to manage without services. A social worker visiting very regularly appeared to hold this situation together. Our interviewer commented:

They have tremendous trust in her now because she has respected their immense need for independence.

Carers with one respite service

Less than a third of the carers in the sample had only one type of respite. They cared for elderly people who were generally more disabled and disturbed than those without respite. Day care was the most common form of respite for this group and direct examples of carers using day care only are provided in Chapter Five. About half of the carers with a single respite service had day care, about one-fifth used a sitting service, and about one quarter had relief care.

The characteristics of the elderly people with day care only and sitting were broadly similar, apart from the reluctance of the latter to attend day care. For example, Mr Harris looked after his wife. They had one son who visited at Christmas and Easter or on birthdays. His wife had attended the local day hospital rather reluctantly and eventually, in Mr Harris's words, had managed to convince him 'she preferred his company' and had given up going. In addition to problems with her memory, her mobility and sight were poor. However, she was a friendly woman who spoke of her husband with affection and enjoyed reminiscing about their past holidays together. Mr Harris had never been offered relief care and indeed, would never 'think of such a thing'.

He took a pride in the fact that he cooked all the meals, did the washing and housework. On Monday afternoon a sitter visited from 2.00 to 4.00 p.m. and he was able to do the weekly shopping at the local supermarket. Occasionally, he saw a community psychiatric nurse and the psychogeriatrician.

The carers with relief care only differed markedly from those with just one home-based break. They formed a younger group and they were more likely to show signs of psychological strain. Their relatives needed help with most of their personal care and showed a high number of trying behaviours, such as restlessness or repetitive questions.

For example, Mrs Barton looked after her 89 year old mother. Both widows, her mother had moved into Mrs Barton's flat eight years ago. Three years before the first interview, she had noticed a deterioration in her mother. Six months later, her mother had a stroke which left her with very poor mobility. She was also in the most dependent category as measured by the BRS. She could not remember her mother ever seeing either a psychogeriatrician or geriatrician. Despite her mother's double incontinence, Mrs Barton had been unable to persuade her to use pads. The parts of caring she found difficult were:

> *Trying to dry clothes [because of incontinence], clearing up [after episodes of incontinence]. Being woken up every night .... When she won't eat, if she starts screaming and tries to hit [me].*

Mrs Barton was very isolated and nearly all her social contact was with her brother, who sat with her mother for two hours weekly. Her mother had had two stays in a nearby local authority home. These had been arranged by the social worker when Mrs Barton had felt like 'running away'. The social worker was now considering arranging regular relief breaks. Up until three months before the first interview, Mrs Barton's mother had been going to that same home for day care twice a week but she had then refused to attend. Mrs Barton had never been offered a sitter, but felt that she would benefit occasionally from such a service so:

> *[I] could go on outings .... or shopping .... [I] have no life of my own .... I'm not able to do anything.*

Carers with two types of respite

Three-quarters of the carers with two types of respite had a package of day and relief care. The number of carers with day care and sitting was small and similar to the number with sitting and relief care. The carers with day care and sitting had more in common with those whose single respite service was day care or sitting, than with those whose package included relief care.

For example, Mr Leith and his wife had been married for 54 years. They had one daughter who lived some distance away but visited and telephoned regularly. It was she who had first suspected dementia when Mrs Leith began to leave notes reminding herself what she needed to do dotted throughout the house. Mrs Leith was on medication for angina and attended the out patient department of the nearest hospital. Respite services had been arranged by the social worker. Just over a month before the first interview, Mrs Leith had started attending the local day centre, albeit with some reluctance at first. While she was there Mr Leith enjoyed the chance to:

> *Stay in and relax without anyone [i.e. his wife] saying 'What are you doing that for?'.*

On Monday morning the sitter visited for an hour. Mr Leith enjoyed the chance to talk to the sitter and appreciated her willingness to take his wife out shopping. He had not been offered relief care and felt that, not only would his wife become distressed if she were to go to a home for a short stay, but also that he would not be able 'to keep away' and so neither would benefit.

The carers who used relief care combined with day care or sitting looked after the most dependent and disturbed group of elderly people in the sample; they were a younger group than those with home based breaks and they were more likely than others to have symptoms of psychological distress.

For example, Mrs Hartnell looked after her 87 year old mother, Mrs Glade, who had moved into her household following widowhood 17 years earlier. Mr Hartnell and their daughter were also resident. Two years before, Mrs Glade had been diagnosed as having Alzheimer's disease:

> *It's very sad .... She realises there's something wrong - she is at the worst stage [i.e. while she still has insight].*

Five days a week, including weekends, Mrs Glade went to day care at a local authority home. Five months before being interviewed for the first time, Mrs Hartnell had arranged two relief breaks in a private home. Then the officer-in-charge of the local authority home had suggested that her mother had relief care in the home as well as day care:

> *When we got there she said, 'I know this place, I don't like it' .... [but] you definitely need the break ... The more she goes into [relief care] the better I feel. The first time, you feel more like a criminal.*

Following this break, Mrs Hartnell was looking forward to beginning a programme of regular relief care arranged by the officer-in-charge.

Compared to the elderly people with day and relief care, the small group of elderly people with sitting and relief were less mobile and had been considered too physically dependent or behaviourally unsuitable to attend day care. The carers and elderly people had most in common with those using relief care only, and are adequately illustrated by the example of Mrs Barton which was described under the previous heading.

The carers with three respite services

The differences between the group with day, sitting and relief care and the group with day and relief care were slight, and most of the 17 per cent of carers in the sample with this package lived in Area Three, as explained earlier.

For example, Mr Derwent looked after his 80 year old wife. He found helping with personal care less difficult than her wandering and poor sleep pattern. A local authority home help came once a week to clean the house. The sitting service had begun two years previously and the sitter visited for five hours once a week. This enabled him to go out shopping or to meet friends. When Mr Derwent was admitted to hospital for emergency surgery his son had arranged for his mother to be looked after in a local authority home. Since then, Mrs Derwent had stayed in Colebrook Lodge, another local authority home, nearby. She spent six weeks at home and two in Colebrook Lodge. Mr Derwent felt:

> *Six weeks is about as long as I can go without having a break ... [I] visit virtually every day [but I am] relieved of the responsibility.*

Like Mr Derwent, some of the carers with and without respite services were also using other community services which we briefly describe under the next heading.

Use of other services

Although the main focus of the study was respite care, we asked the carers about their use of other community services. Our results confirm that respite care is part of a wider package of services made up of practical help, professional advice and cash benefits.

Home help

Twenty six per cent of the elderly people and their carers had been allocated home helps and six per cent had made their own arrangements for domestic help. Most of those with private domestic help lived in Area One. By contrast, similar proportions of carers in the three areas had been allocated home helps. The receipt of the home help service did not vary with the number of respite services used.

Importantly, there was a strong link between the characteristics of the carers and their use of the home help service at the first interview. Typically, the carers who had been allocated home helps were elderly husbands and wives who lived in two person households and who had disabling conditions.

For example, half of the carers aged 75 and over, compared with only 15 per cent of those aged under 75 had home help services. Strikingly, two thirds of the carers assisted by home helps had disabilities themselves. Thus the service assisted a very vulnerable group of carers who were determined to look after their partners for as long as possible. It was not surprising, therefore, that these carers were more likely than others to have a package of domiciliary services. Half of those with home helps were also assisted by bath nurses and a third of them had sitting services. We have emphasised the differentiating characteristics of the carers with home help because we shall refer to them again in Chapter Eight and show what had happened to these carers and their elderly relatives a year later.

Community nursing services

Sixty three per cent of carers had nursing services. Thirty seven per cent were visited by community psychiatric nurses, 24 per cent were visited by district nurses, 16 per cent by bath nurses and four per cent by health visitors. Elderly people without respite were less likely to be assisted by district nurses or bath nurses than others. This finding was not surprising as those without respite were more physically able. The likelihood that carers were assisted by district nurses did not vary by area; by contrast, 20 per cent of elderly people in Area Three had bath nurses, compared with eight per cent in Area Two and with seven per cent in Area One.

Meals and laundry services

Only eight per cent of the elderly people and six per cent of the carers had the meals service. As might be expected, most of these were elderly couples who were also assisted by home helps, but a few younger carers who were in paid employment had meals delivered to their elderly relative on the days that they were out at work. Most carers were at home all day and liked to do their own cooking. There were only six carers who would have liked meals delivered to them but had not been offered the service.

Only four per cent of the carers used either health, social services or commercial laundry services. Most carers had their own washing machines and very few wanted a laundry service.

Carers' groups

Twenty eight per cent of the carers had been to at least one meeting of a special carers' group. Organised by voluntary organisations or professionals, these groups are a relatively new way of supporting carers, providing the opportunity to share experiences with other carers and to obtain advice and information. The carers who used day care services were most likely to have attended a meeting of a carers' group. Almost half of those with an intensive package of respite services had been to carers' groups.

Attendance Allowance and Invalid Care Allowance

Seventy per cent of the elderly people in this sample had successfully claimed Disability Living/Attendance Allowance, about half of them at the higher and half of them at the lower rate. Given the criteria for eligibility to claim this cash benefit, this finding complemented our evidence on the high levels of dependency of the elderly people in our sample. As degree of dependency was associated with the number of services used, it was not surprising that the proportion of elderly people with this allowance rose from just over one in five of those without respite to over three in five of those with one service and four in five of those with two and those with three services. As well as Attendance Allowance, 11 per cent of carers claimed Invalid Care Allowance, that is just over one third of the carers who were below pensionable age.

Summary and closing issues

Our preparatory work for this study revealed a dearth of systematic information about the users of respite services across health, social services and the independent sectors. Our research has established the characteristics of one group of users, namely people with dementia who live with their carers, across agencies in three localities. Clearly, the focus of the study meant that we did not collect information on the full range of people with each and every type of respite, such as might be required to plan, allocate and monitor services fully. We believe, however, that the value of this sort of exercise is underlined by the results of this part of our study, as summarised here.

Firstly, we have confirmed that the carers with respite services were looking after a group of very dependent people.

Secondly, we have shown that over half of these carers used a package of two or three respite services.

Thirdly, we have shown that the most common package of respite in each of the three areas was day care combined with relief care.

We have provided substantial evidence that different packages of respite services were targeted on people with differing degrees of dependency and behavioural disturbance. The carers in our study were looking after one of the most disabled groups of elderly people in the community. In this context, the carers who were not using respite services looked after elderly people who formed the least dependent group. Those with two or three respite services were coping with the most dependent elderly people; and those using one service occupied an intermediate position.

It was encouraging that psychogeriatric teams and social workers were involved with carers and elderly people who were not using any of the respite services. Our results suggest that elderly people are being identified by general practitioners and referred for assessment, practical help and continuing support at a point when there is a possibility of beneficial interventions, rather than when the carers had already reached breaking point.

The concentration of packages of respite at the heavy end of the dependency continuum may also seem reassuring, confirming that services were targeted on those in greatest need. However, even though relatively intensive packages of respite were said by the carers to make their lives more tolerable, the cost to them of continuing to care was often great, and they showed, on average, higher levels of psychological stress than others. A further consequence of concentrating intensive packages of respite on groups of very dependent people and on groups of psychologically distressed carers was that there were fewer opportunities for the services to be used to prevent the build up of strain in other carers.

Finally, we have shown that respite services are often delivered as part of a wider package of care made up of assessment and support by doctors, social workers and community psychiatric nurses, practical help from home helps, district nurses and bath nurses, and cash benefits, such as Attendance and Invalid Care Allowance.

5   Day Care

It's a burden being lifted off my back when she goes to day care.

Twice a week would be nice - it would break the week up.

Background

In the United Kingdom, day care is one of the main community services for people with Alzheimer's disease and other forms of dementia. Pioneered over forty years ago, day care services have grown rapidly and in a piecemeal fashion since 1970. Health and social services, the voluntary sector and, uncommonly, the private sector have each separately developed their own provision. As a result, there is wide variation in the amount, source and type of provision across the country. Day care is offered in day hospitals, in specialist and ordinary day centres, in nursing and residential care homes, on hospital wards and, innovatively, in bungalows and in the private homes of individuals.

Tester (1989) provides a widely accepted definition of day care which encapsulates the common elements of the services offered in a range of settings, and distinguishes them from day facilities which offer company, educational and leisure services:

> *A day care service offers communal care, with paid or voluntary caregivers present, in a setting outside the user's own home. Individuals come or are brought to use the services, which are available for at least four hours during the day ....*

These services are assuming increasing importance as the policy of community care is implemented. Their development is officially encouraged, and the independent sector has been identified as the major provider of day care for the future. These developments have re-fuelled the debate about the aims, organisation, content, quality and effects of the service and have stimulated interest in the information available from research in the UK and other countries (Age Concern, 1992; Brearley and Mandelstam, 1991; Gilleard, 1992; SSI, 1992).

Previous work

Research has raised a number of issues which are relevant to the development of day care services in the future.

[63]

First, research has shown that elderly people with dementia are more likely to use day care services than others up to and including the last year of their lives (Cullen *et al.*, 1992; Farrow, 1992).

Second, several studies have drawn attention to the overlap in the objectives, programmes and users of day hospitals and day centres (Levin *et al.*, 1989; Pahl, 1989; Nies *et al.*, 1991). Theoretically, day hospitals concentrate more on assessment and therapies than day centres where the social aspects of the service is emphasised. In practice, this distinction has become blurred.

Third, two types of day care users have been distinguished with one group using the service for a short period, usually as a precursor to residential care and the other group using it for longer and being looked after by carers who find the service very helpful (Gilleard *et al.*, 1984; Salter, 1992).

The next issue concerns the effects of day care services on admissions to residential care and on a carer's mental health. A small but growing number of experimental and comparative studies have tackled these questions (Gilleard, 1987; Lawton *et al.*, 1989; Levin *et al.*, 1989; O'Connor *et al.*; 1991, Wells and Jorm, 1987; Wells *et al.*, 1990). In broad terms, they have suggested that the service may delay the admission of some elderly people into residential care for longer periods than others but cannot entirely substitute for it. They conclude also that day care cannot bring benefits to a carer's mental health equivalent to the benefits from residential care. They point out that this result is understandable, given the limited amount of time off afforded by day care and the chronic and progressive nature of dementia. Consistently, these researchers draw attention to the carers' positive views of the service, and to its contribution to their quality of life.

Day care in the study areas

Day care was the main service providing the carers in the sample with a regular break on a weekly basis. In all three areas, the elderly people and their carers were far more likely to have day care than they were to have sitting or any of the other domiciliary services. At the first interviews, 67 per cent of the elderly people were going to day care regularly, and a further 13 per cent had gone in the past; only six per cent of the carers had not been offered this form of respite.

The day care services allocated to these elderly people depended upon where they lived in several respects. First, in Area Three more of the sample of elderly people attended day care (77 per cent) than in Area Two (63 per cent) and in Area One (60 per cent). This difference was partly explained by relatively higher levels of day care provision in Area Three and by referral practices. Second, the sector of services most likely to be providing the elderly people with day care varied between one area and the other two. Figure 5.1 shows that the majority of elderly people in Area One had day care provided by the health services; by contrast, the majority in Area Two and in Area Three had day care provided by social services or the voluntary sector.

Figure 5.1 Source of Day Care by Area

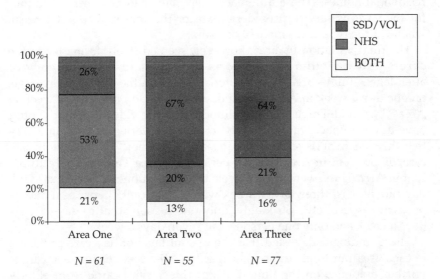

There were differences, too, between the areas in the likelihood that day care was provided by social services rather than by the voluntary sector. Just under 20 per cent of the elderly people went to voluntary sector day centres: elderly people in Area One were least likely to have social services day care and those in Area Three were most likely to have it.

Figure 5.1 shows also that in each area, a minority of elderly people had some of their day care provided by the health service and some of it provided by the social services and voluntary sector. We shall return to the issue of overlap in the sources of day care later in this chapter.

A third and inter-related difference between areas was the setting in which day care was provided. The elderly people with day care in the sample were looked after in one or more of the following: day centres (53 per cent), day hospitals (46 per cent), residential homes (19 per cent), day clubs (six per cent) and, in the case of two people only, on hospital wards. Consistent with the variation by area in the use of health service provision, the majority of day care attenders in Area One went to day hospitals and the majority in the other two areas went to day centres. In addition, almost one third of those with day care in Area Three went to residential homes for this service, whereas only very small minorities of the comparable groups in the other two areas had this type of day care.

The above differences arose mainly from the way in which services had evolved in the three areas, with one sector, for example, developing their day care provision to compensate for deficiencies in other sectors; they also reflected differences in policies on day care in local authority residential homes. These differences may have had greater implications for the various service providers than for the carers, who got a break whatever the type and source of day care.

The final variation by area, however, seemed likely to matter to the carers and the elderly people, as it concerned the frequency of attendance at day care. Day care took over from the carers, on average, on one day a week in Area One and, on average, on two days a week in Areas Two and Three. The likelihood that the elderly people would have day care once, rather than twice, a week varied by area in a way that their characteristics and circumstances did not. Of those with day care, 57 per cent in Area One, 24 per cent in Area Two and only 10 per cent in Area Three went once a week; the proportions in these areas with day care at least three days a week were 12 per cent, 37 per cent and 42 per cent respectively. Strikingly, only one person went to day care six days a week and only one person went seven days a week.

These findings suggested that the overall level of day care provision in each area put limits upon the capacity of the services to assist carers. Further evidence on the limitations of this service came from elderly people in the sample who had day care at two venues, either in the same sector or different sectors of the services.

In each area, one quarter of the day care attenders were looked after at two - or in a few instances, three - different places each week. Such packages included care in both a centre and a hospital, care in two centres, one of which was run by social services and the other run by Age Concern or Alzheimer's Disease Society, and care both in a local authority or private home and a centre or hospital. The health service was the only provider of day care to almost one third of families, the other two sectors were the providers for just over one half of them, and the health service in partnership with others provided day care for the remaining minority.

We have discussed the reasons for these arrangements with professionals in the areas. They have pointed out that some day care units only catered for people with dementia on particular days of the week and that day care in the late afternoon, the evening or at the weekend was generally only provided in residential homes. Day care at more than one place was arranged because some carers required more time off than one unit or sector could provide. Few professionals seemed to think that such arrangements were likely to be in the best interests of the elderly people. The practice seemed to have grown up in an ad hoc manner and out of necessity; it did not appear to have been the subject of much joint discussion or policy making by the various agencies.

We shall return to these issues when we bring together our findings which suggested that day care was under-provided. Meanwhile, it should be noted that, when carers wanted the service several days a week, the 'care managers' had the time-consuming task of devising a package of day care from different sources, sectors or both. They also had the task of devising wider packages of respite care services.

Day care as part of a package

Three out of four carers who had day care services were also using other respite services. It is important to take account of these wider packages of respite because they were targeted upon different groups and outcomes for their users varied.

For some purposes, therefore, we divided the day care users into smaller groups: first, there was a group made up of 24 per cent of the elderly people who went to day care but did not have sitting or relief care; second, there was a small group of eight per cent who had day care and sitting services; the third and largest group was comprised of the 49 per cent of day care users who also had relief care; and the final group was comprised of the 21 per cent of day care users who also had both sitting and relief care. The most important distinction, as we will show later, was between the seven in ten day care users whose package of respite care included short stays away from home and the three in ten day care users whose package did not include them.

Day care only

There were more carers in the sample with day care as their only form of respite than there were carers with sitting only or relief care only. The majority were looking after a husband or wife and the situation of Mr and Mrs Mortimer was typical of this group.

Mr and Mrs Mortimer were an elderly couple whose lives had been made easier by the timely provision of day care. It was their general practitioner who had first explained Alzheimer's disease to Mrs Mortimer and suggested day care for Mr Mortimer, aged 83. Then, as his wife said: 'it all just happened'. She had accepted the offer because:

> Well, I suppose it was all getting on top of me. The doctor said some of my problems were due to stress ... and everyone thought it was a good idea.

Arrangements were made for Mr Mortimer to go to a social services day centre on Tuesdays and Thursdays. He was collected by the ambulance at about 9 a.m. and returned at about 4 p.m. Mrs Mortimer, aged 80, and married for over 40 years, had been worried about sending her husband to day care at first. As she explained:

I felt guilty about putting him out and wondered if I had done the right thing.

Day care enabled Mrs Mortimer to go out with her friends, be more relaxed and, 'feel freer'. She was always pleased to see her husband on his return. She was very complimentary about the staff at the centre, which she had visited, and she had been told she could come at any time. She knew the names of two members of staff:

Madeleine, I think is in charge, and I have met Jack - he takes my husband's group.

Mr Mortimer had enjoyed going to day care from the start. He did not talk about it very much when he got home but he was able to tell the interviewer what he liked and disliked about it:

Talking to different folk is the chief thing ... the two people who lead it are very canny (nice) folk. There is one grumpy man ... the meals are good ...

This couple's only other practical service was a home help once a week for two hours and Mrs Mortimer would not have accepted relief care. Their general practitioner's skill, in recognising signs of strain in the carer and prescribing day care as a partial solution, seemed to have greatly benefited this couple. Day care had stabilised a deteriorating situation in a way which was acceptable and enjoyed by both partners.

The acceptability of day care to many elderly carers, and its provision in response to strain and increasing dependency, became very clear when we compared the characteristics of those who had day care services and of those who did not.

Allocation of day care

Under this heading, we shall consider three questions with implications for policy on day care. First, who went to any type of day care? Second, what were the similarities and differences between those who had day care but not relief care, and those with both day and relief care? Third, what were the differences, if any, between those with day care from the health service, those with day care from social services and voluntary organisations, and those with day care from both the health service and other sectors?

Any day care or no day care

Table 5.1 shows that, among those with and without day care, the level of cognitive impairment in the elderly people, as measured by the CAPE

Information and Orientation Test was about the same. By contrast, the elderly people with day care had experienced persistent problems with memory and orientation for a longer period than those without day care.

Table 5.1 shows also that day care was targeted on the more dependent elderly people in this sample and on those who had a higher number of major behavioural and interpersonal problems. This would be expected from our previous discussion of the links between the characteristics of the elderly people and the number of respite services used.

Table 5.1 Characteristics of the Elderly People by Use of Day Care

	With day care	Without day care	Total	Significance
	Mean	Mean	Mean	
Information and orientation score	5.07	5.61	5.24	t value 1.16 $p = 0.249$
Number of months with memory problems	65.56	48.22	60.00	t value -2.76 $p = 0.006$
BRS score	17.77	14.76	16.77	t value -3.82 $p = 0.000$
Major behaviour problems score	3.23	2.6	3.02	t value -3.14 $p = 0.002$
Total sample (N)	*193*	*94*	*287*	

The likelihood of attendance at day care did not vary with the age, gender or marital status of an elderly person; by contrast, the likelihood of attendance at day care increased with the degree of dependency of the elderly person on their carers and others, as measured by their scores on the Behaviour Rating Scale of the CAPE. For example, 55 per cent of the elderly people with day care, compared with 34 per cent of those without day care had BRS scores which fell into the severe dependency category of the CAPE. The elderly people who were particularly likely to go to day care were those who could not work out how to do basic tasks, who were incontinent, apathetic, and physically disabled; not surprisingly, therefore, the greater the amount of help with personal care required, and the greater the number of behaviour problems manifested, the greater the likelihood of attendance at day care.

It was interesting that we found a strong link between the number of behavioural and interpersonal problems of an elderly person and the use of day care, especially because the degree of cognitive impairment in an elderly person was not associated with the use of day care. This finding

suggested that day care was used to give a carer a break from an elderly
person whose behaviour was at times very difficult to tolerate.

Although day care services were targeted on very dependent elderly
people, it was encouraging that they were also allocated to about half of
those who were, on several measures, less dependent in the context of
this sample.

Table 5.2 Characteristics of the Carers by Use of Day Care

	With day care	Without day care	Total	Significance
	Mean	Mean	Mean	
Age	64.84	69.62	66.41	t value 2.91 $p = 0.004$
Number of years living with elderly person	32.43	39.62	34.79	t value 2.7 $p = 0.007$
Number of personal care routine carer helps with	5.35	4.49	5.07	t value 2.21 $p = 0.029$
Number of hours apart from elderly person each week	19.19	9.92	16.16	t value -4.8 $p = 0.000$
Total sample (N)	*193*	*94*	*287*	

A wide range of carers, too, used day care. For example, 72 per cent
of the daughters and 63 per cent of the wives and husbands had day care
services. However, Table 5.2 shows that the carers with day care were a
younger group than the carers without day care. The carers were most
likely to use day care if they perceived themselves as very restricted and
if they had lived with the elderly person for less than five years. Thus,
83 per cent of the carers who had lived with their elderly relative for less
than five years, compared with 64 per cent of those who had lived with
them for at least five years had day care services.

Day care only or day and relief care

Our second question was whether there were any differences between
the carers and elderly people using both day and relief care, and those
using day care but not relief care. In broad terms, our findings
confirmed how packages of respite were tailored to carers'
circumstances and built up gradually as the carers' problems increased,
as we have discussed in Chapter Four.

Day care without relief care seemed to occupy an intermediate
position in the spectrum of respite services. In many respects, the
elderly people and their carers who had day care only were more

similar to those without any respite services than they were to those with day and relief care. Thus, elderly people with day care only were, on average, younger and more likely to be looked after by a spouse; they were also less cognitively impaired, less physically disabled and less behaviourally disturbed; not surprisingly, their carers showed fewer signs of emotional distress and perceived themselves as less restricted.

Overlap in the sources of day care

Our third question concerned whether day care from the various sectors was targeted upon different groups of elderly people. Our tentative conclusion must be that in this sample the area where the carer and elderly person lived was the strongest predictor of the sector of service allocating day care, as shown in Figure 5.1. There was some evidence that elderly people whose dependency levels were very severe indeed were more likely than others to have both a combination of health service and other day care. In addition, the carers who definitely would have accepted residential care were more likely to have day care from two sectors, and so, too were those who had day care at least four days a week. It seemed, therefore, that a combination of health service and other day care was being used to provide elderly people on the margins of residential care with an intensive day care service, usually combined with relief care. Overall, however, with the exception of where they lived, the characteristics of the elderly people with day care from different sectors were similar.

We were not greatly surprised by this overlap between sectors: social services provision for confused elderly people in one area was scarce, units in the most rural area were scattered, and day hospitals were used mainly for assessment in the other. In addition Pahl (1989) and Nies and his colleagues (1991) have reported similar findings. Undoubtedly, there were historical reasons for this overlap. It may, however, have to be recognised and addressed if a coherent pattern of local day care services is to be developed.

Finally in this section, we highlight one finding which shows that the allocation of day care had an impact upon the carers' everyday lives: the use of day care was a predictor of the total number of hours that most carers and elderly people spent apart from each other each week, as shown in Table 5.1. Thus, only 25 per cent of those without day care were apart for more than eight hours each week as against 86 per cent of those with day care. Furthermore, as we had expected, the number of hours apart each week rose sharply with the number of days of attendance at day care each week. For example, attendance at day care resulted in the elderly people being away from home, on average, 14 hours per week; time away rose from, on average, six hours for those who went to day care once a week to, on average, 30 hours for those who went four or more days a week. It was hardly surprising, therefore, that the break afforded by day care was highly valued by the carers.

The carers' reactions to day care

Day care took over from the carers, on average, for 14 hours each week. Their reactions to this break left us in no doubt about the relevance and the benefits of day care services.

First, three in ten carers with day care had used the service for at least two years; and half of this group had used it for at least three years. Second, one third of those with day care had accepted one or more extra days of service per week since its commencement. And third, once they had obtained day care, most carers continued to use it until they no longer had to look after their dependent. Thus, at the first interview, only one in ten of the carers had taken up the service and stopped it, and the main reason for terminating the service was an elderly person's refusal to attend; and at the second interview, the carers' main reasons for no longer using day care were that an elderly person had gone into a home or a hospital or had died.

The vast majority of carers (92 per cent) with day care considered that the service had brought about some improvements in their lives; half of them described how day care had made a lot of difference to their lives. For example, Mrs Yelloly said that day care had made her life:

> *One hundred per cent better than it was. It's complete freedom. She's out of the house and I'm completely free for six hours. I can stay in or go out.*

This carer's comment on her sense of freedom when her mother went to day care was echoed by many others. There were some interesting variations on this theme. Mr Oliver, looking after his wife, valued:

> *The freedom of not having to check up on her.*

Mrs Reckitt did the same things when her husband was at day care, 'but with a freer mind', than when he was at home; and Miss North said:

> *On the days that I'm free, i.e. from my mother, I go and look after an aunt.*

For the carers, there were advantages to be gained from sending the elderly people to day care rather than leaving them at home with sitters. The carers had more choice about whether they stayed at home or went out; and day care generally gave them a longer break in any one day than that given by sitting services. Thus, if they used day care, they were able to shop in a more leisurely manner, and to engage in a wider range of activities in the morning and afternoon.

Most carers used the time when their relatives were at day care to engage in ordinary, everyday activities which were difficult or even impossible to do when the elderly people were at home. They shopped, paid the bills, went to the hairdressers, met friends for lunch, visited relatives, went to church and played bowls. They also stayed at home and did the housework, pursued their own interests, or simply rested, enjoying some time to themselves.

Only a few carers said that day care did not make any difference to their lives. One of these explained that she was too exhausted to do anything, and another commented that she left her husband alone at home anyway; others were already going out to work before day care was arranged or were unsure about the impact of regular day care because assessment at a day hospital had just started.

By contrast, the majority of carers with day care valued the regular, reliable weekly breaks it afforded to them. Importantly, most of these carers thought that day care also benefited their relatives. For example, Mrs Sanford, looking after her mother, said:

The benefits apply to us both. I am able to relax and she is occupied.

Some elderly people would hardly ever have gone out of the house were it not for day care. At the very least, as the carers often said:

It's a day out from the four walls.

Day care, according to the carers, gave the elderly people a change of scene, some company and some stimulation. Although many elderly people did not say anything about day care on their return home, some carers had detected an improvement, albeit small, in their relative's appearance, mood or behaviour. For example, Mrs Dain said of her husband:

He comes back brighter. They keep his mind going.

One in three carers with day care thought that their elderly relatives had benefited greatly from day care. They described their relatives as happier, as more relaxed, as more confident, as more talkative, and as showing more interest in people and events. Mr Sulker's wife went to a day centre where each elderly person had an individual care programme, and activities were tailored to past interests. In his view, the benefit to her was:

It's slowed her down from being senile. She has a sense of purpose.

Like the carers, our interviewers were unable to get every elderly person to tell them what they thought about day care because some could not even remember that they attended. Nonetheless, it was certainly worth asking the elderly people, whatever the degree of their cognitive impairment, what they liked and disliked about day care. Although some said that they liked the meal, or the outings or talking to a friend, others told the interviewers quite a lot about their time at day care and their enjoyment of it.

For example, Mrs Hay, aged 89, was looked after by her son, who was single and in his fifties. She was incontinent, very disorientated and forgetful but she reacted with a great deal of enjoyment to our interviewer's visit. She went for day care to a residential home twice a week and told the interviewer:

> *I like to go there ... they're nice up there. I do all the washing up but the staff don't let you do much. I'm there to rest ... I read the paper ... I wouldn't be afraid to go and stop with them - they're so nice.*

Some carers had only agreed to day care in the first place because they thought that it might benefit their relatives; some had been persuaded by professionals that they needed a day off; and others had accepted because they were at breaking point. For example, Mrs Bates's reason for accepting day care was:

> *I couldn't have gone on without it. It enabled me to keep him at home.*

The carers identified social workers and community psychiatric nurses as the professionals most likely to have suggested day care to them. Their comments showed that skilled, patient work on the part of practitioners was often required if the transition to day care was to be achieved. The carers reported most frequently that their relatives had been anxious and apprehensive about day care at first; however, by the time of the first interview, most carers said that their relatives went happily, or at least without protest. Likewise, some carers had felt guilty and anxious about sending their relatives to day care at first; by the time of the first interview, few remained guilty and anxious, and most were pleased when the elderly people left for day care.

The benefits of day care to some carers lasted beyond the six hour's break. Often, the elderly people were tired on returning home and so their carers had a peaceful evening or even a full night's sleep. Most frequently, the carers described their relatives on their return as seeming pleased to be home and to see them.

The carers' reactions to their relatives' return were more varied. They included feeling apprehensive, for example, 'about what sort of a mood she'll be in', feeling resigned to, 'starting all over again', and feeling, 'more rested and ready to cope'. Typically, however, they described themselves, as they had the elderly people, as pleased to be reunited. Mrs Hayley combined her comment on her reaction to her husband's return home with a comment on day care in general:

I'm pleased to see him - this is why it's so good.

Suggestions for improvements

The data from the first interviews with the carers suggested that there were three areas in which there was scope for improvements in day care services: first, professional practice at the point when day care was being arranged, second, the quality of the service, and third, its availability and flexibility. Each of these areas is covered in the wide range of suggestions for improvement set out in a recent Social Services Inspectorate literature review (Brearley and Mandelstam, 1992). They are also covered in a recent detailed guide to the standards of day care that older people should be able to expect (Age Concern, 1992).

Arranging day care

The first set of improvements were concerned with the **timing** of an offer of day care, providing the carers with more **information** about day care, giving them some **choice** about when and how often they wanted the service, and **preparing** the carer and the elderly person for day care. They were highlighted by the following findings:

Timing We asked the carers to estimate when the elderly people had first shown persistent memory and orientation problems and we also asked when they had first started to use day care. Over 30 per cent of those with day care had been caring for periods of up to four years before day care began.

Information Only one quarter of the carers using the service said that they had been given some written information about day care. Usually, this had been given in the form of a booklet which could provide a handy reference point.

Choice Less than one fifth of the carers with day care said that they had been asked how often they would like their relatives to attend day care. Only one fifth of the carers with day care had been asked which days of the week they would have liked their relatives to attend.

Preparation Only one third of carers with day care said that a member of staff from the day care unit had visited them at home before their elderly relatives had begun to attend. Likewise, only one third said that either they or their elderly relatives, or both of them had visited the day care unit before taking up the service.

It may not be possible to achieve some of these improvements without more resources in terms of staff and day care places. For example, carers cannot choose when the elderly people have day care, if units only cater for people with dementia on particular days of the week, and new users have to take up the place on the day previous users attended. Booklets cannot be produced if staff do not have the time to prepare them or the money to print them. However, some changes may be possible within existing resources, for example, by a different use of staff time and other strategies.

At the very least, the information that we have provided on the variation in practice among day care providers offers a benchmark against which any team or unit may evaluate their own practice.

Quality of day care

Improvements in the quality of the service were concerned with the day care programme, the provision of transport and the promotion of partnerships between the carers and the staff at day care units.

The day care programme The carers who were well-informed about the elderly people's activities at day care praised units where each elderly person was a member of a small group and had a key worker responsible for them. They also praised units where the elderly people were busy most of the day, where they engaged in a wide range of activities, and where they were taken out regularly. They were more likely to report that their relatives derived a lot of benefit from going to day care if they knew that the elderly people had a varied programme of activities and outings. The carers with experience of two different units sometimes compared one of them unfavourably with the other. For example, Mrs Bowes said:

> I would like them to have more things to do at (the day centre). They look so old and unstimulated. My husband likes it at (the day hospital), but not at (the day centre).

The provision of more stimulating programmes is likely to depend upon improvements in the management and training of day care staff. Some carers recognised this need and pointed out that a particular unit did not have enough staff to provide individual attention, or that the staff lacked experience in working with confused elderly people, or that the turnover in staff was high.

Criticisms were made of some centres run by voluntary organisations because the volunteers changed too frequently; and criticisms were made of the system whereby day care was terminated in one centre or home because the staff could not cope with an elderly person's behaviour. However, these criticisms were greatly outnumbered by positive comments. For example, praise was given to social services centres where everyone had a key worker; and praise was given to a centre where everyone got a lot of individual attention because the ratio of volunteers to elderly people was one to one.

Transport Most elderly people travelled to and from day care in ambulances, buses or cars provided by the services. Their carers were very pleased with this arrangement, and many would have been unable to use the service without it. They also understood the difficulties of providing an efficient service when the traffic could be unpredictable and there were a lot of elderly people to pick up. Some of these difficulties were beyond the control of the services. For example, Mr Hay said of his mother:

She will dirty herself just when they come to collect her for day care.

About 70 per cent of the carers with transport services said that they had not experienced any problems with the transport. For example, Mrs Elswick said:

They've always turned up. They've never said they would come and didn't; they are the most reliable people.

The carers of elderly people who had health services day care were most likely to have had problems with the transport. As we had expected, the main problem was the timing of the service. Some carers would have liked a more reliable service. Often, they had to rise early in order to get the elderly people ready for day care and it was frustrating, therefore, when they had to wait longer than expected for the transport, or when it failed to arrive at all. Mrs O'Hagan said:

They're unreliable about time - we have to have her ready by 8am as the ambulance sometimes arrives early but sometimes she is still sitting ready till 9.30am.

The improvements suggested by this group were more predictable times of collection and return, and telephone calls when the transport was cancelled or delayed. Others would have liked a more flexible service so that, for example, the elderly people could leave for day care after 10 a.m. and return after 5 p.m. The minority of carers who were able to take the elderly people to day care themselves enjoyed this degree of flexibility. They also had more contact with the staff at the day care unit and, in one area, they could have day care as often as they liked; however, as some of them pointed out, the journey there and back twice a day was an extra chore and reduced the length of their break.

The provision of transport has been identified as one of the most problematic issues for day care services and also, as a major item of the total expenditure on day care. Some day care managers have told us how they have managed to achieve a service which is both reliable and flexible:

they provided day care very locally so that the journey time was short, and they had a minibus with a driver and escort attached to the centre throughout the day so that they were able to make separate journeys to collect one or two elderly people at times convenient to their carers.

Promotion of partnerships between carers and day care staff The comments of some carers suggested that the quality of the carers' experience of day care might have been improved by more collaboration between the carers and the day care staff. This need was most apparent among carers who did not take the elderly people to day care.

First, it was surprising that two in five carers with day care did not know the name of any member of staff at the unit that their relatives attended. Second, two in five carers had not discussed their relatives' progress at day care with either a staff member or another professional. Usually, telephone conversations were brief and confined to practical matters, and messages were passed between the staff or the carers by the ambulance driver or the escort. Whilst many carers were satisfied by this arrangement, some would have welcomed the opportunity afforded to others to attend a meeting to discuss their relatives' progress or to have advice from experienced staff. Mr Grillings said that the improvement that he would most like to see in the service was:

> I'd like to know how she is (when at day care) and how she behaves compared to how she is at home.

Availability and flexibility

The final set of suggestions for improvements in day care were concerned with the **availability and flexibility of the service**. On our evidence, the requirements for day care among some users and also among some non-users of the service were unmet.

Carers with day care First, we have shown that the carers were provided with day care, on average, one day per week in one area and, on average, two days per week in the other two areas. We have also shown that most carers with day care valued the service highly. Therefore, it was not surprising that one half of the carers with the service would have liked their relatives to go to day care more often.

Usually, the carers' requirement was for one extra day to bring the service up to two to three days per week. For example, Mrs Maddison said that: 'One more day would make a difference'. However, some carers would have liked several extra days. As Mrs Mullen, looking after her husband, remarked: 'It sounds greedy! Every day would be lovely'.

In this study, a day care package of four or more days per week was targeted on carers who had used the service for many months, often in combination with relief care, on those who looked after a severely dependent elderly person and on those who showed signs of great strain. Also, there were waiting lists for extra days at some units. We noted earlier that day care showed promise as a service with beneficial effects on the carers' psychological health. It was difficult to see how the services in the study areas could have realised this potential unless day care provision was expanded.

Further resources, too, would have been required to provide the more extended and more flexible service which some carers would have liked. Three in ten carers with day care would have preferred the service at different times than the times they had been allocated it. Unless they went to residential homes for day care, most elderly people left for day care before 10 a.m. and returned home between 3.30 p.m. and 5 p.m. Some carers would have preferred a full afternoon and evening to themselves and others would have preferred 'afternoon care' five days a week. Yet others would have chosen different days to have the service, had it been possible. Mr Victor commented:

> *I had to make a fuss to get her there on a Tuesday - they wanted her on a Friday but that wasn't convenient to me.*

We were not surprised to find that there was an unmet demand for day care at weekends. Only five per cent of the elderly people with day care went at the weekend, and only three people went on both Saturdays and Sundays. By contrast, on Mondays, for example, half the elderly people with day care were attending. Typically, daughters, daughters in law, and sons, including those in paid employment, were the carers who either had or would have liked day care at the weekends. Mrs Percy said:

> *Weekends would be helpful so I can go out with my husband.*

The need to extend day care services so that they are available at weekends has become more widely recognised. Special funding has stimulated new initiatives in which paid staff and volunteers provide a service at weekends in units which would otherwise remain closed.

Carers without day care In this study the findings which suggested that day care was under provided came mainly from carers who were using day care services. However, among those without day care, there were carers who had already used the service, carers who were about to start using it, and carers who would have liked the service.

We stated earlier that the great majority of carers in this sample were using or had been offered day care. This finding was not surprising, given the sources of the sample and the wider availability of day care as a weekly form of respite. However, it should be seen in the context of the comparable proportions offered other forms of respite: it will be shown in the following chapters that the carers were far more likely to have been offered day care than they were to have been offered sitting or relief care. Among the carers without day care, one fifth had not been offered it and two-fifths had used the service in the past; at the first interview, 13 per cent of the elderly people without day care were about to use the service for the first time.

The carers' main reasons for having refused or stopped the service in the past were the elderly people's dislike or their refusal of the service, as other studies have also shown (Levin *et al.*, 1989; Farrow, 1992). Likewise, their main reasons for not accepting the service at the time of the interview were that the elderly people would not want it. However, half of the carers without the service thought it would have brought about improvements in their lives of the sort which those with the service valued. One third of the carers without day care would have liked it.

It was difficult to see how the carers' requirements for day care could be met, given that most of those without day care thought that their relatives would not be willing to attend. However, some of the offers of day care had been made many months ago and the carers, having refused then, were reluctant to ask for the break they later realised was necessary. There was scope for offering the service again and for attempting to get the elderly people to accept it. Moreover, there was scope for trying to substitute a sitter for day care, so that the carers could have the benefits of the break enjoyed by those with day care services.

Closing issues and summary

Day care is the main service which provides a regular weekly break for the carers of people with dementia. It will continue to occupy this central position until sitting and carer support services expand and become less patchy. Even then, it seems unlikely that the importance of day care will diminish, for it has the unique feature of caring for the elderly people during the day away from home. Thus both day care and sitting services, which can complement and substitute for each other, will be necessary if the support system for carers in each area is to be comprehensive and flexible. As summarised below, our study raises a number of policy and practice issues which may require attention if the objective of delivering high quality day care services is to be achieved.

Policy issues

The broad policy issues highlighted by our findings on day care include the following:

Availability The overall mix and level of day care provision for elderly people with dementia varied between areas. These differences were reflected in the type and frequency of service allocated to those with day care.

Overlap Health, social services and voluntary organisations were providing day care in each area for some elderly people and carers whose characteristics were quite similar. The area in which the elderly people lived was the strongest predictor of the sector of the services providing them with day care. A substantial minority had day care provided by both health services and other sectors. Joint planning and collaborative work between agencies would be required, therefore, if a coherent pattern of day care services is to be achieved. There was scope also to develop locality-based rather than sector-based services.

Allocation In general, day care, particularly when combined with relief care, was targeted on heavily dependent elderly people and on carers who showed signs of great strain. Thus the policy requirement to target services on those in greatest need and their carers appeared to have been met: in consequence, however, opportunities to use the services to maintain the well-being of other carers, and the abilities of other elderly people were limited.

Day care as part of package Most carers with day care also used other respite services. The most common package was day and relief care. The care management task, therefore, involved the construction and monitoring of packages of respite. The departure of some elderly people to relief care regularly raised the question of the use of the day care places in their absence.

Underprovision Day care provided most carers with a break once or twice a week. Many carers required more frequent breaks and an extended service during the day or at the weekends.

Practice issues

The practice issues requiring attention were highlighted by the variation in the quality of the service received by elderly people and their carers. There are several steps which might be taken to ensure that practice matches up to the best that we have seen and that has been described to us. These include trying to ensure that, wherever possible, carers are:

  informed about local day care services and how to obtain them,
  referred by general practitioners and others to the professionals who arrange day care,
  offered day care at an early stage,
  given some choice about the amount, timing, and frequency of the service,
  given written information about the day care unit,
  given the opportunity to visit the unit with their elderly relatives or to be visited by day care staff,

told the names of the staff, and told about the unit programme,
invited to review the elderly people's progress at day care,
encouraged to seek the advice of day care staff if they wish,
informed when **transport** is cancelled or delayed,
encouraged to ask for extra day care if they need it,
and **offered** other forms of breaks if day care is unsuitable.

Most of these improvements can be achieved within existing resources. However, further resources would seem to be required to secure two important developments. These are first, the extension of day care services; and second, the provision of high quality day care services.

The carers in our study looked after a group of very dependent elderly people. Many relied on day care as their only source of a break each week. They greatly appreciated the service for the help it gave both to them and to their elderly relatives. The theme which ran through the carers' comments on day care was that it had made life a lot easier. This opinion should be taken seriously. We shall discuss day care further when we examine the effects of respite services on the carers' psychological health. In our view, the value of the service to the carers in our study strengthens an already strong case for the provision of day care services for elderly people with dementia and their carers.

6   Sitting and Carers' Support Schemes

The only way I can have a few hours away.

Background

Sitting and carers' support schemes should be included among the more recent developments to community care services. They have an especial contribution in that, unlike day and relief care, assistance is offered to the carer and person cared for *within their own home*. Moreover, the emphasis of many schemes on providing a service for the *carer* highlights a way in which they may be differentiated from home care and home help services.

Many schemes throughout the country have developed in an ad hoc way in response to local need. This has resulted in a diversity of provision ranging along a continuum from, at one end, befriending services usually provided for a few hours once a week by volunteers to, at the other, paid workers who may carry out intensive personal care spanning over several days or nights each week. The reality is that distinctions between services may blur as each adapts to the prevailing circumstances in its own area.

Emphasising this type of local variation has become a byword in descriptions of sitting and carers' support schemes. Some of this may be attributed in part to differing service aims. Is the scheme designed for specific groups, such as people with Alzheimer's disease? Is the intention to provide more intensive assistance to a proportionally smaller amount of people or limited service time to a relatively extensive group? In addition, recruitment or funding issues may have an impact.

Thus, our outline so far suggests that nationally our picture of sitting and carers' support schemes is disparate and unclear. There is one further important reason for this. Unlike day or relief care, sitting and carers' support schemes have yet to be part of mainstream provision. Instead, funded in the short term, operating on a small scale, such services may experience the contradictory difficulties of initial under-use at the same time as uncovering previously unidentified need.

Do we have clearer ideas about who is providing these services? Theoretically, of course, they may be operated by local health authorities and social services departments, voluntary and not-for-profit organisations and private agencies. In practice, most are run by voluntary organisations, often with statutory sources of funding. Although there is an increasing number of private agencies offering this sort of service, it would still be fair to note that, where carers have organised and paid directly for privately arranged sitters, this has more often been the result of an informal arrangement between the carer and a person such as a former residential care worker or nurse.

Terminology

The variety of terms used to describe respite services provided within the home reflects each scheme's individual purpose and emphasis. Additionally, in order to reduce the possibility of a mismatch between carers' expectations and the service which will actually be provided, some schemes have deliberately and carefully chosen the names of their service and workers, hence the distinction noted earlier between befriending services offering companionship and care attendant schemes which may include an element of personal care.

While acknowledging the validity and usefulness of these distinctions, for convenience we shall use the term 'sitter' throughout the rest of this chapter except where reasons of clarity require otherwise. The text will make it clear where the discussion refers to sitters from voluntary or statutory organisations, privately arranged services or both.

Previous work on sitting schemes

Much of the existing literature has, more often than not, taken the form of accounts by the scheme's workers or articles for trade journals. Essentially, their intention has been to inform and stimulate discussion, as in the account of an Edinburgh sitting scheme (Barry, 1988). Furthermore, because provision remains limited, reviews have tended to extend across care groups and appraisals have had to be broadbased in their scope.

Early accounts suggested that the development of sitting services was a response to gaps in existing provision, for instance because of the increasing numbers of carers who needed a break but did not want relief care in an institution (Rosenvinge *et al.*, 1986).

Probably the most well known example is the Crossroads Care Attendant Scheme (Bristow, 1986). Although affiliated to a national federation, local schemes have organisational differences. Reviews of the literature have suggested that, on the whole, the focus of care attendant schemes, whether affiliated to Crossroads or not, is still upon younger disabled people (Twigg *et al.*, 1990).

Comparisons of befriending and care attendant schemes have suggested that the former are biased towards less dependent people.

Because they tend to use volunteers assigning a few hours of their time per week to the service, their co-ordinators need to recruit and train around one volunteer per family (Haffenden, 1991).

Across all types of schemes, availability is currently very varied. The suggestion that there is unmet need was made by the House of Commons Social Services Committee, quoting from the evidence given by workers from a Crossroads Scheme in the Wirral, in its Fifth Report (1990). An average of four hours help was given each week. Unfortunately, such was the demand, some of those on the waiting list had been caring for *10 years* with no help at all.

A similar picture emerged as part of a canvass of Alzheimer's Disease Society members. Recognising that the respondents may not have been typical of all carers, the report nevertheless expressed great concern that few carers had any type of sitting service. Furthermore, the *respite* provided was limited in that typically carers remained on hand to assist the sitter, and the service was restricted to an hour or two per week (Hart, 1991).

Another survey of consumers' views carried out across two health districts concluded that among the most frequently mentioned areas of need was a sitting service for people with dementia (Wyn Thomas, 1990).

One of the most comprehensive accounts of sitting services remains Thornton's account of the Age Concern 'In Safe Hands' scheme in York (1989). Since its inception in 1981, most of the scheme's resources were allocated to services for carers. In addition to a paid part-time organiser, it was staffed by helpers who were paid a fee designed to be more than tokenistic but less than current market rates. Care could be provided both day and night, for a short time or for continuous periods up to two weeks, within the elderly person's (or occasionally the helper's) home. She ascribed the scheme's success to its ability to ensure that the views of those using the service were taken into account, that services were supportive and tailored to an individual's needs and choices, that the contribution of helpers was valued and the care they provided was of a high standard. Although unable to reach objective conclusions about how far the scheme was able to maintain carers in their roles, the study concluded that examples existed where a breakdown in community living had been avoided. Overall, the scheme *filled a gap* in, rather than *substituted* for other community services.

Enhancing and complementing existing local provision was the identical intention of the North and West Belfast Dementia Project which was set up to provide a service to people with dementia and their families (Reid, 1992). For 20 per cent of the carers who were interviewed, Extra Care (as the service was termed) was the only help they received. Average service times were three or four hours per week.

This account contains several important messages which are echoed in other studies. Nearly all the carers were daughters or daughters in law of the person for whom they cared. A focus upon carers in the younger age group has also been noted in Twigg *et al.*'s review (1990). Despite local publicity, few referrals came from carers and, at first, the number of referrals from whatever source was very low. Although the hours of service were limited, Extra Care was useful as a point of contact in terms of monitoring change and referring on to other services. Consistency in staffing was key and a need was identified for both a regular and an occasional service. For instance, some carers particularly praised the system whereby they telephoned early in the morning to arrange for a sitter that afternoon. However, there were a number of refusals or 'non-starters' (for instance, if the person went into residential care) and Reid concluded that it was important to continue to monitor service uptake.

New services will always be in a vulnerable position as they seek to establish themselves. While the need to provide sitting services overnight is often mentioned, attempts to arrange such services have often been short lived. It is noteworthy that the one example of a comparatively well known and long established scheme, the night visiting service which is part of the Govan Dementia Project, was set up to extend and improve *existing* assessment and day care arrangements (Illsley, 1992). However, Illsley also points out that no figures were available to see whether there was a *demonstrable* decrease in the number of admissions to hospital, although it is well thought of locally and has received a national award.

Two studies in the United States have suggested that one advantage of sitting services (in-home respite) was their ability to deal with people with Alzheimer's disease of varying levels of severity (Brody *et al.*, 1989; Ehrlich and White, 1991). Another study suggested that receipt of sitting services often led to use of other community services but that the high numbers of people entering residential care or dying within a few months of starting to receive the service suggested that it was often offered as a 'last ditch attempt' to prevent admission to residential care (Gwyther, 1989).

All three studies cited above commented that at one end of the scale, extended or overnight home-based respite can become an extremely costly option, while at the other, services which only offer companionship do not meet the higher levels of help required by carers of people with dementia.

Taken as a whole, the literature suggests overwhelmingly that sitting schemes are appreciated by carers, can complement (but not substitute) for other services and that, for a scheme to be successful, attention must be paid to ensuring that sitters' personal qualities, reliability, experience and training are such that carers feel able to welcome them into their homes. However, what is lacking is information on their usefulness and relevance from *evaluative* studies (Twigg *et al.*, 1990).

Another difficulty in assessing the impact of sitting schemes is that they are rarely provided at highly intensive levels yet there are questions to be raised concerning the limited relevance to carers of a service which they may receive for only a few hours per month (Leat, 1992). Moreover, she adds, the fact that such schemes are still often classed as innovative:

... says something important about the time it takes to become 'established' and widely accepted, and about the precarious existence of many areas of work whose value is not in dispute.

(Leat, 1992, p.94)

Types of scheme in the study areas

Consistent with the picture outlined above, there was considerable variation between the schemes in the study areas. This was not just related to hours of service receipt but extended right across organisational and funding issues, systems for reimbursing staff, and what the carers might expect the sitters to do.

Area One contained the largest scheme. At the time of the study, it was jointly funded by the health authority and social services department but was organised by the local branch of MIND. It was staffed by a director, a part time co-ordinator, a part time secretary and 45 sitters. All these posts were salaried and the sitters received a flat rate payment for the hours they worked. Funding by the Mental Illness Specific Grant had enabled a 'companion' service to people with dementia living on their own to be set up. The longer established part of the scheme was the provision of a sitter to families of people with dementia. The service times were negotiated between the director, co-ordinator, carer and sitter and theoretically could be provided at any time during the day and evening, weekdays and weekends. A limited night service had been in operation for a time but was withdrawn during a period of funding uncertainty.

Area Two had a scheme which was established for some time, jointly funded by health and social services and organised by Age Concern. In the months before the carers were first interviewed, the introduction of Employment Training had led to a massive reduction in the number of sitters available. Much of their role was taken up in visiting elderly people living on their own, especially in preparing them for day care. Where carers received a service, the sitter's role was essentially one of befriending or companionship. However, by the time that the follow up interviews were completed the service was divided into two parts. One co-ordinator organised the people on Employment Training who visited the frail elderly. The local health authority took responsibility for funding a second co-ordinator and a team of sitters paid a weekly honorarium who visited elderly people with mental health problems.

Area Three was the one study area where several types of service existed. There were two carers' support schemes, funded by the local authority through grant aid, but organised by two local voluntary organisations. The schemes aimed to provide a service to frail elderly people with a recognised, but not necessarily resident, carer. Users of the schemes were visited by care attendants who worked part time for payment at rates comparable to people working in local authority residential homes or home care departments. The care attendant's task was to 'do anything a caring friend or relative would do' so work might consist of freeing the carer to go out or helping him or her with shopping or the elderly person's personal care.

A voluntary organisation receiving its funding from grant aid and local donations ran a Community Warden scheme. Its aim was to provide a 'service which might be offered by a good neighbour'. The wardens were all volunteers who were paid a nominal fee. Users of the service usually lived alone and so only one carer in our sample used the scheme.

The local branch of the Alzheimer's Disease Society also ran a sitting scheme. Due to changes in funding at the time that the sample was selected, only one carer in the sample was using this service. However, the funding was later integrated with that for day care and each new referral was assessed to see whether day care or sitting should be offered either separately or in combination. Although the co-ordinator's post was paid, the sitters themselves were volunteers paid a notional amount.

Lastly, Age Concern ran a sitting scheme for resident carers and a visiting service for elderly people on their own. The service was not restricted to certain groups; the only criteria was that the person cared for was over 65 and that the carer was unable or unwilling to leave him or her for any significant length of time. The sitters were all volunteers reimbursed only for their travelling expenses.

A small proportion of carers in all three study areas used private sitting services. In nearly every case this was the result of informal arrangements. For instance, one carer used an agency until, upon its closure, she turned to friends who had worked in nursing or residential homes.

Use, types and sources of sitting services

Of all the respite services which we studied, sitting was used by the smallest number. Only 30 per cent of the carers and elderly people in the sample were visited by any type of sitter. This varied tremendously by area, as is shown in Table 6.1.

Our earlier description of the schemes in the study areas has already given an indication of the types of service available. The scheme in Area One was the one in which the aim of providing respite to carers was most explicit. In Area Two, it was essentially a befriending service, a source of social support but rarely of time off from caring. Carers in Area Three had limited access to sitters in that the Age Concern and Alzheimer's Disease Society schemes had to cover a large geographical area and were reliant upon volunteers. The Warden Scheme was unlikely to be providing a service to the type of carers in our sample. Most of the carers with sitters in this area used one of the carers' support schemes restricted to certain geographical areas and providing a service to *all* the frail elderly. The timing and frequency of sitter visits and the types of task undertaken suggested that this type of service fitted more nearly into the care attendant model.

Table 6.1 Area Comparisons and Receipt of Sitting Services

	% With sitter	N	Significance
Area One	42	42	
			chi-sqr 11.86
Area Two	19	17	
			$P= 0.0027$
Area Three	27	26	
Total in sample with sitter	**30**	*85**	

*This figure includes sitters from any source.

In contrast to day and relief care where the NHS and social services departments were major providers, over 80 per cent of carers with a sitter were visited by someone from a voluntary organisation. This is not to say that the sitters themselves were volunteers. Indeed, if we exclude those who were on Employment Training or were paid workers, then we are left with very few indeed. This is entirely consistent with the literature, suggesting that a volunteer service will be unlikely to offer a substantial level of provision to the types of carers in our sample.

Fourteen per cent (n=12) of the carers had made private arrangements and a further three carers used a combination of private and voluntary organisation sitters. The numbers are too small to permit separate analyses of private services; two points only are worth making. The first is that the number of carers with private sitters was spread fairly evenly across the study areas. The second is that, in all but three cases, the carer had made an informal arrangement him or herself and not used an agency.

In two cases, we were unable to ascertain the source of the sitter, other than verifying that it had not been privately arranged.

Timing and frequency of visits from sitters

The amount of time that carers could expect to receive each week from sitting services was extremely limited. Using the carers' information, we calculated that the mean length of time per week from sitters from voluntary organisations was just over three and a half hours, just one quarter of the equivalent period that an elderly person might spend at day care which was two days.

In Area One, carers were generally visited weekly. The shortest visit lasted two hours but half of the carers had visits of four hours or more. The mean length of service time here was four and a half hours.

In Area Two, a weekly visit was also most frequent. The mean length of visit was one and a quarter hours. The maximum level of provision was three visits each week lasting three-quarters of an hour to a man whose son was in full time paid employment.

Carers in Area Three might expect to be visited once or twice a week, amounting to a mean total of three and a quarter hours. The shortest time allocated was divided between two visits. For the first, the care attendant called to see the carer and stayed for a quarter of an hour or so. During the second, because the carer was in poor physical health, she spent an hour doing the carer's shopping. The maximum service time was ten hours per week, allocated to a woman whose parents both required high levels of personal care.

When examining the service given by sitting and carers' support schemes there is a further aspect which must be taken into account: the times of day in which they were operational.

Not a single carer received the service on a Sunday and just four were visited on Saturdays. Furthermore, nearly all these visits took place during the day time. Only five carers had sitters of an evening (and one of these was so the carer could attend a carers' group). In addition to this, one sitter picked up the elderly person from day care, accompanied her home and waited until the elderly person's daughter in law returned from work. Thus the visits were, in the main, only taking place between the hours of 10 a.m. and 4 p.m.

Carers who used private sitters were able to negotiate more easily the timing of visits. For instance, one daughter paid friends who had worked in residential homes to come and look after her mother at night; 'at least [you can] get your sleep', she explained. The mean length of time per week from privately arranged sitters was, at just under eighteen hours, much higher than the equivalent time from voluntary sitters.

Set against this, we must consider the fact that very few carers indeed were actually receiving such a service. Furthermore, the costs to the carer must also be taken into account. None of the voluntary agencies charged carers directly for the sitters' visits. The cost of private sitters was variable, ranging from £1.50 to £10 an hour! The mean cost per hour of private sitters was £3.50. Two carers used money from the Independent Living Fund to pay for this service; in every other case it was the carer or elderly person who was paying.

So why should there be such disparities between the amounts of service time received by carers using voluntary and private sitters? The answer lies in the need of the co-ordinators of voluntary schemes to juggle constantly with the limited amount of service hours available. Each scheme generally operated on the basis of having a set amount of hours to allocate each month. As the co-ordinators explained, if they were to offer a particularly intensive package to one carer, then this could only be at the expense of limiting the service to others.

Sitting as part of a package

The use of sitting in conjunction with other respite services was extremely frequent. Thus, our question is not so much whether carers had a sitter or not, but with what other forms of respite was the service combined?

Among carers with sitters the most unusual package was that of sitting and relief care, used by just 15 per cent. It was found particularly among carers of people too physically frail or behaviourally difficult to attend day care. As evidence of this, well over half of those cared for would be dead by the time of the follow up interviews.

The combination of sitting and day care was used by 18 per cent of carers. By contrast, they were generally looking after people who were less dependent and often had only become known to services within the past year.

Twenty per cent used sitting services only. The people they cared for were generally similar to those using day care and sitting. The difference was that a high percentage of the elderly people in this group had refused to go to day care.

The largest group, almost half of those with a sitter, used all three respite services. As we have explained earlier, this was essentially an area difference rather than a reflection of the characteristics of those cared for.

There was also a strong relationship between having a sitter and receiving home care or privately arranged domestic help.

Taken together, the evidence outlined above suggests that the place of sitting as part of a package is, as the existing literature confirms, one of complementing rather than substituting for other forms of provision. The allocation of these packages gave strong support to the views of the co-ordinators who explained that one purpose of sitting and carers' support schemes was to provide respite to carers of those who were deemed to be unsuitable, too physically frail, or had refused to attend day care.

Allocation of sitting services

An important point to remember when considering the allocation of sitting services is that many schemes in the study areas focused upon

providing a service for *carers* and it is often to their characteristics that
we must look to see the most sharply defined differences, rather than
those of the people they cared for.

Having said this, it is important to recognise that sitting services were
targeted upon elderly people needing greater help with their personal
care and showing greater dependency, as measured by the BRS. Such
factors would have a considerable impact upon whether they could be
left alone by their carer, as we shall discuss later.

Table 6.2 Characteristics of the Elderly People and Receipt of Sitting Services

	Sitter	No Sitter	*t* value	Significance
Mean BRS Score	18.17	16.16	-2.44	0.0015
Mean number of personal care routines carer helps with	5.8	4.76	-2.8	0.005
Total (N)	**85**	**202**		

The mean age of carers with sitters was 63, over four years less than
the equivalent figure for carers without the service. Only 25 per cent of
spouses who cared had a voluntary organisation or privately arranged
sitter. Yet we have seen that spouses comprised the highest proportion
of carers. This difference would seem to be largely explained by the
greater number of adult children who had arranged for a private sitter
and suggests that sitting services were under provided to the
disadvantage of a large proportion of carers.

On a more positive note, the co-ordinators of voluntary organisation
schemes explained that one criteria they used for allocating sitters was
social isolation resulting from the carer being unable to leave the person
they cared for alone in the house. Table 6.3 shows that sitting services
were targeted upon those who reported the most social restrictions
through caring. As we have seen earlier, the likelihood that, if
unsupervised, the person cared for would have been unable to go to the
lavatory, make a drink or may even have done something potentially
dangerous, such as leaving a tap on, was greater for elderly people with
sitters. Therefore, reluctance to leave them on their own was not
misplaced over-anxiety on the part of the carer but a very legitimate and
real concern.

Interestingly, receipt of a sitter was not related to carers' GHQ scores,
raising the possibility that the schemes were not responding reactively
once the probability of psychiatric morbidity was evident but were
taking a positive, preventative step to deal with the very real problems
of social isolation experienced by many carers.

Table 6.3 Carer Restrictions by Use of Sitting Services

	% With Sitter	% No Sitter	Total (N)	Significance
Elderly person left alone				
Yes	18	82	139	chi-sqr 8.006
No	33	67	144	p = 0.005
Carer has felt lonely				
Yes	32	68	119	chi-sqr 4.814
No	20	80	166	p = 0.028
Seen enough of family/friends				
Definitely yes	22	78	64	chi-sqr 11.956
Probably yes	20	80	65	p = 0.008
Probably no	15	85	55	
Definitely no	37	63	100	
GHQ score from carer's interview				
GHQ 0-5	25	75	173	chi-sqr 0.077
GHQ 6-28	26	74	114	p = 0.781
Total	**25**	**75**	**287**	

Carers' reactions to the sitting service

Nearly everyone with a sitter felt that their lives had been improved. Willingness to accept a sitter could stem from a combination of reasons. First, time off from caring was felt to be important. As one daughter explained:

[I was] desperate for a break - clutching at anything.

Second, a recurrent comment was the difference it made to be able to go out and know the elderly person was safe. In the words of one wife:

It's made it easier. I can have my hair done and relax for a few hours.

It is important to note that even among those carers who *did* leave the person they cared for alone, he or she was left on fewer occasions and for shorter periods of time than those elderly people without sitters. This supports the carers' feelings that they needed the sitters' visits for more time-consuming activities such as going shopping, paying bills or visiting friends or family.

Third, initial apprehensions about leaving the elderly person faded away as carers became used to the service. The descriptions of their reactions the first time the sitter came and their current feelings were significantly different; feelings such as guilt and worry changed to pleasure and anticipation. One husband said simply:

I've got something to look forward to.

The daughter of one of the carers who died in the period between the first interview and the follow up, shared these feelings:

> *At first my mother felt reluctant to leave him. You feel it's your responsibility but then she began to look forward to it. Two days before she died she said, 'I really look forward to my afternoon off'. You can't quantify that sort of help which you get from the sitting service. [Other] people offer to help but you know they couldn't cope because of the unpredictability of people like my father.*

This comment also embodies a fourth reason why carers were willing to accept a sitter. Many carers felt that the particular problems posed by dementia made it harder to ask a family member or friend to look after the elderly person.

Not every carer with a sitter had initially welcomed the idea. Over a third of carers with sitters from voluntary or statutory organisations said that it was discussion with a social worker, community nurse, psychogeriatrician or other professional which had persuaded them to try the service. One wife actually stated that she had not felt that she needed the service, but seeing the disappointment on the co-ordinator's face, agreed 'just to make her feel better'! However, she admitted that she needed the service to enable her to go to the bank and the hairdresser every Friday afternoon.

Many carers mentioned that, as well as needing the regular visits, an occasional 'extra' service to enable them to go out for the evening or attend a family celebration would be very helpful. One daughter looking after her mother explained that, because the sitter visited while she was at work, her 'mind was a bit freer at work' but she could not feel any real benefit from the service because there was 'no service for **me**'. A smaller number of carers would have wanted a night service. This seems to suggest that greater priority should be given to extending day and evening services, rather than embarking on overnight schemes when existing provision is not yet adequate.

Our examination of packages of respite suggested that sitting services had a valuable role to play in helping carers of people recently diagnosed as having Alzheimer's disease. Using the carers' estimate of onset as our starting point, we found that sitting services had, on average, started *four* years after the symptoms consistent with a diagnosis of dementia had first become apparent. Of equal concern is the variability within this figure. Almost 30 per cent of carers had started receiving a sitter within a year of their estimate of onset, yet 20 per cent had been caring for over *six* years before the service began. This implies that there is room for expansion in sitting services so that they can fulfil their potential in acting as a useful entry point for other community care services.

The elderly people's reactions to the sitting service

Nearly 60 per cent of carers saw benefits to the elderly person, as well as themselves, in having a sitter. The advantages of the company of another person or stimulation for the elderly person if the sitter took him or her out were mentioned most often.

One man, who was looked after by his wife, was able to talk directly about how he found his sitter:

> [We] sit and chat about all subjects ... She comes to me. I don't have to bother going out.

The elderly people often mentioned enjoying talking to the sitter and sharing a cup of tea. Friendliness and being cheerful were also valued. An elderly person explained:

> It doesn't matter who comes I forget them but it doesn't matter with her ... She tells us that much I can't take it in. This time she was full of her moving.

Her husband said later that he thought this was a reference to the sitter having a new job. Another woman was more resigned to the sitter's visits:

> Once this person came in. She didn't do anything. I suppose she'll be coming regularly.

Improvements to sitting services

The carers' suggestions for improvements to the service centred around two themes. The first relates to the amount and timing, the second to the practices around the delivery of the service.

We have emphasised already the limited amounts of time per week carers might expect to receive. Therefore, we were not surprised that almost half the carers with sitters would have liked the service more often. Furthermore, 32 per cent would have liked the visits to last longer. This was especially true for carers who used the sitters' visits to enable them to pursue hobbies:

> [It would] give me more time to do things, go to choir practice.

The limited amount of time available from sitting helps explain why so few carers reported that they were able to use the sitters' visits to remain in full time employment.

This first set of comments have direct implications for the funding of sitting schemes. The second suggest that, irrespective of resources, some aspects of service delivery could be improved.

An important consideration for carers was whether the sitter was the sort of person they felt happy to have in their home. Nearly every carer had something favourable to say about their regular sitter but just 14 per cent stated that they had been given some say in the type of person who would be visiting. One practice that varied very obviously between the schemes was whether the carer had had an opportunity to meet the sitter before his or her first visit. Just *one* carer in Area One did not remember having done this. As a wife living in Area One said:

> *It was all done properly. They were brought [round] and introduced so you had confidence in them being in your own home.*

By contrast, a husband in one of the remaining areas where this practice was, on the basis of the carers' reports, less frequent said that his sitter:

> *... just arrived on the doorstep but as she was from [scheme] I just thought she must be alright.*

Reliability was another quality by which carers set store:

> *Having the same person each week is great. I wouldn't like lots of different people.*

Nearly every carer had a regular sitter and changes in staffing or holiday arrangements were the most frequent reasons for having a different person. Most carers were warned in advance if the sitter were unable to come but in only about half the cases had a substitute been provided.

Given that many carers needed time to become familiar with the idea of a sitting service, it was important that they received written information to help them in their decision making. Across all three study areas, only 25 per cent of carers remembered receiving a booklet or leaflet about the scheme. Admittedly each scheme produced annual reports on their service but they were more useful to existing users and it is possible that many carers would have benefited from a short leaflet about what sort of a service they might expect.

One final topic relevant to voluntary organisation sitting services is that, taking into account the fact that they may be expected to provide a service to carers who are themselves frail, they may be faced with a decision over whether respite for the carer involves a physical separation from the person cared for, or whether it is a way of sharing the carer's workload, even if this means that he or she does not take a specific break from caring.

Carers using two of the schemes mentioned that they had to go out while the sitter visited. While ideal for active carers who had pre-arranged plans, some carers would have preferred to stay at home and rest or work in the garden uninterrupted. It should be noted here that in our review of previous work on sitting, the practice of expecting carers to stay with the sitter was specifically criticised by some carers. Therefore, there is no easy answer to this question and schemes will constantly have to re-evaluate their approach.

For those with private sitters, because so many arrangements had evolved at the carer's behest, issues such as timing and introductions were of less importance. The most frequent criticisms of agency staff related to personnel changes, reiterating the importance of having one regular person.

Carers who chose not to use sitting services

Just over 25 per cent of carers without a sitter had either been offered or had ceased to use the service. Some carers were still undecided whether to accept or not; others were due to start. Five carers had asked for the service, only to be told it was not available or to have heard nothing more.

Only eight carers had actually given up the service once it had started. Some of the reasons for refusal were reluctance to have a stranger in the house, fears that the sitter and elderly person would not get on, or an inconvenient time. One 84 year old wife explained that she had decided not to have a sitter because:

> *I read all the conditions and thought it would take a week to get ready!*

Carers without sitting services

An indication of the way in which sitting services remain outside the mainstream is that so few carers had ever been offered, or were even conversant with the idea of a sitter. By contrast, day care was a service familiar to everyone, irrespective of whether they actually used the service.

A third of the carers without sitters said that they would like to have such a service, either regularly or occasionally. Taking into account the fact that the idea was a novelty to many carers, this is an astonishingly high proportion. Furthermore, the carers most likely to want a sitter were adult children who often had competing responsibilities, those who had given up hobbies or felt restricted by caring, and carers with high GHQ scores. This suggests that there is an unmet need for sitting and raises the wider issue of how much carers' preferences can influence future provision of services.

Closing issues and summary

Only a third of carers received any sort of sitting service. Nearly all the sitters came from voluntary organisations and the time that they could provide each week was very limited. This picture is entirely consistent with the literature, suggesting that sitting services have yet to become part of mainstream community care provision.

Carers using sitting services valued them highly, particularly for the way in which the service freed them to get on with essential household tasks such as shopping and paying bills.

The availability of sitting services varied throughout the study areas. This was a matter of concern as it seemed that many carers and elderly people who may have benefited from sitters had never been offered the service.

The allocation of sitting services suggested that they were relevant to a wide range of carers. On the one hand, sitting services may offer a valuable contribution to people who have been recently diagnosed as suffering from dementia, acting as an entry point for other community care services and monitoring change. On the other, they can be helpful to carers looking after more dependent elderly people who may be unsuitable for day care. Unfortunately, limited provision means that the potential of home based schemes to offer a long term service for carers of people with dementia has yet to be realised.

Taking into account the numbers of carers who wanted sitters more often and those who would have liked to have the service at all, then it seems clear that, if community care services are to pay attention to carers' wishes and needs, it is essential to make developing home based respite services a key priority.

7   Relief Care

*Looking forward to a break and knowing that she would be
alright was like a breath of fresh air.*

Background

For many people, the arrangement by which a person who is usually
looked after by a carer spends time temporarily in some form of
residential care is the type of respite with which they are most familiar.
It may seem strange, therefore, to go on to say that, of all the services we
examined, this is the one which lends itself least easily to a simple and
universally agreed explanation.

Relief, respite, short term, short stay, holiday, and rotating care are
just some of the terms which have been used to describe this type of
care. Since we completed the study, the Social Services Inspectorate has
issued a guidance document with the following definition:

> *A short-term break is an arrangement whereby children or adults who are
> normally dependent upon regular carers for at least some aspect of their personal
> care and support, are provided with a break from their primary carer for a short
> period. This may include residential, domiciliary, and home supported assistance.
> Short-term breaks cover at least one night of care but will not exceed three months
> in the case of adults and no more than four weeks continuous care in the case of
> children. They will address both the personal and social care of the users. They
> will always be or become part of an integrated, reviewed, programme of support
> which is appropriate.*
>
> (SSI, 1993, p.4)

While we acknowledge the validity of the viewpoint that words such
as 'respite' and 'care' could be seen as having pejorative connotations by
ascribing negative attributes to the person cared for, such as being
burdensome or dependent, we shall use the term relief care as it seems to
describe more precisely a period of short term care whose chief aim is to
relieve the carer of his or her caring responsibilities.

Finding an agreed, acceptable definition is not the only problem. A
further difficulty lies in distinguishing between relief care admissions
and any other type of short stay. It is sometimes difficult to differentiate

those whose primary purpose is relief for the carer and those which take place for other reasons, such as assessment or rehabilitation.

In making this distinction the criterion which we used was that giving the carer a break had to have been an *explicit* purpose of the elderly person's admission to short term care but need not have been its *sole* purpose.

Provision of relief care

Sources of relief care are currently varied but, at the time of writing, placements within institutions substantially outnumber those in other settings. This is most usually achieved either by allocating designated beds within a home or hospital ward or by providing a specialised unit. Relief care may be provided by local authorities, the NHS, voluntary organisations or the private sector.

It is difficult to quantify the amount of relief care available through NHS sources because, in addition to specially designated beds, it may also be provided at the discretion of the consultant (Twigg *et al.*, 1990). Geriatric and psychogeriatric services are both providers of relief care but one review quoted an estimate that as little as seven per cent of all respite was provided in hospitals (Griffith, 1993). Department of Health estimates for 1989–90 (1993) classify less than 30,000 admissions of people over the age of 65 as holiday relief care, a tiny fraction of the overall total.

The Department of Health's study (1991) of residential accommodation for elderly and for younger physically disabled people contrasted the percentage of short stays in local authority homes, which numbered 62 per cent of admissions in 1980, but had risen to 78 per cent in 1990. It pointed out that no distinctions could be made between the number of *persons* admitted and the number of *admissions* each person had. Younger physically handicapped people were also included in the figures. Even allowing for such provisos, it would seem evident that relief care occupies a central position among local authority mainstream services to carers.

Information on relief care in private or voluntary homes is currently limited but that which does exist suggests that it remains small scale. Using the same Department of Health figures, as of 31 March 1990, just over two per cent of residents in voluntary homes for the elderly and for younger physically handicapped people were short stay residents. At one per cent, the equivalent figure for private homes was even smaller (1991). Additionally, it should be acknowledged that this figure only relates to one point in time and does not necessarily reflect the proportion of short stays in each private or voluntary home over the year. At a local level, there may be greater variation. One study of private residential homes in Norfolk suggested that a third were providing short term care (Weaver *et al.*, 1985). It must be recognised that, compared with other forms of respite service, relief care demands greater capital and revenue costs and this may be one reason limiting its provision within the voluntary sector. Similarly, residential care proprietors may favour regular revenue from permanent residents, rather than short stay residents whose occupancy rates are likely to be subject to greater variation.

In recent years some local and health authorities, either separately or through joint funding, have sought to provide purpose built units which combine both day and relief services. Examples of these are to be found in the Alzheimer's Disease Society Good Practice Booklet (Burningham, 1990) or within a wider discussion of residential care as a whole (Payne, 1989). Combining day and relief care in one venue is favoured by some because it is believed that this will provide a more seamless service, facilitating continuity of care by staff and a sense of familiarity in those attending the unit (Gilleard, 1992).

Since the late 1970s some local authorities and voluntary organisations have also set up family based respite care schemes (also known as adult placement schemes), described by Carol Robinson as 'any service which provides short term care for a person who is elderly or disabled in a normal, family environment' (1991). Those currently available have concentrated more often on helping children with learning disabilities, although the Liverpool Personal Service Society (PSS) scheme for elderly people has been running for over ten years (PSS, 1993).

Even more unusual at the time of writing are arrangements whereby a worker moves in for a set period with the person requiring care, enabling him or her to receive relief care in his or her own home. In our study, no carers had experienced this type of break.

In summary, the overall pattern of relief care provision suggests that the vast majority is provided in residential settings in local authority homes or the NHS. While alternatives exist, their provision is far more patchy.

Previous work on relief care

The literature on relief care reflects the balance in favour of the provision of care in institutional settings. Two themes have predominated. The first relates to the quality of the care provided and the experiences of the carers and people cared for. The second, to the ability of relief care as a service to enable people to continue as carers. Possibly more than any other community service, relief care arouses some of the strongest feelings and is the one where evidence of its effectiveness is most equivocal and difficult to interpret.

A fundamental obstacle in analysing whether relief care is effective is that carers using the service may experience several, sometimes conflicting, emotions such as guilt, anxiety that the person cared for will not like the venue, loss or a sense of purposeless while he or she is away, but joy and relief that their time is their own (Robinson, 1991; Twigg *et al.*, 1990; Twigg, 1992).

Feelings of guilt can be exacerbated if the quality of care provided is not what the carer would wish. Problems such as lack of privacy, lack of flexibility in the timing and length of stays, choice about the venue, 'matching' the person cared for to a suitable home, mentioned in early studies recur persistently, as later reviews have demonstrated (Allen, 1983; Boldy and Kuh, 1984; Twigg, 1992).

One of the particular problems reported by carers of people with dementia is that the person cared for may return home more confused. The first point to be mentioned here is that the venues in which much relief care is currently offered rarely incorporate design features which have been found to be suited for people with dementia (Lodge, 1990). Second, time should be taken to reassure carers that problems with orientation following a move to less familiar surroundings are to be expected and are likely to be temporary (Murphy, 1986).

In an evaluation of a geriatric unit in Scotland, Primrose and Primrose (1992) suggested that the appointment of a respite care co-ordinator might help improve communication between carers and hospital staff and prevent admissions only occurring in response to crises, such as a change in the carer's health or domestic circumstances. The researchers felt that this was important as patients in this category were more likely to be deemed 'inappropriate' for NHS elderly care wards, had longer lengths of stay (thus 'blocking' beds) and comprised the majority of patients who were not discharged home and moved on to non NHS residential care.

Nolan and Grant's (1992) evaluation of a hospital respite had three useful pointers for improving the quality of relief stays. The first was that targeting services on the basis of assessments of the elderly person's functional dependency has limitations in that this may not be the key factor contributing to carer stress. Second, account must be taken of the carers' expert knowledge about the people cared for. Third, carers' perceptions of a service's quality and acceptability are crucial to their reactions.

The debate about the value of relief care is not restricted only to the satisfaction of those using the service but also encompasses arguments about the effectiveness of relief care in enabling people to continue to remain at home.

Martinus and Severs (1988) studied carers whose relatives had relief stays in a geriatric unit. While carers' energy levels rose significantly during their relatives' stay in hospital, this was not maintained once they had returned home. They also commented on the high rate of drop-out among those using the service.

High non-attendance and fall-out rates were also noted by Melzer (1990) in his evaluation of a purpose built respite unit. Two years after their first assessment, only a small proportion of the original users were still attending. He concluded that this did not lend support to optimistic assumptions about relief care in the long term.

Dunstan (1989) also viewed relief care as having a limited time span. Fifty cases who ceased to have regular relief stays in two geriatric hospitals were compared with a similar group still using the service. The factors contributing to the end of relief care were most commonly medical, reflected in the patients' high mortality and admission to geriatric beds before death. It should be noted here that the finding reported by Rai *et al.* (1986) that increased mortality and morbidity were to be found in elderly people admitted for relief care has not been replicated in other studies.

An earlier NISW study (Levin *et al.*, 1989) concluded that, in addition to making some carers see the advantages of ceasing to care, relief care was also a way of bringing to the attention of social workers or care staff just how great the needs of the person cared for were, meaning that a permanent place was more likely to be offered. Another purpose was to 'ration' permanent places so that relief breaks became a holding operation, ready to be ceased once a permanent place became available. Finally, relief care, targeted as it was upon the more dependent people in the sample, was a way of gradually preparing both carer and elderly person for permanent care. This point was also made in a United States study by Scharlach and Frenzel (1986).

When included among an innovatory package of service provision, relief care did seem to help to maintain people in the community (Donaldson *et al.*, 1988). They compared a group of people attending the Family Support Unit in Middlesbrough with a package of day and relief care, access to a project co-ordinator and other services, with a control group. Service use was higher among those attending the Family Support Unit and they were significantly more likely to remain at home for longer.

Pearson (1988) also suggested that relief care may help to delay permanent residential care for a group of people diagnosed as having dementia. This study was restricted to small numbers (25), because it only included carers who had used the service at least twice and where the primary purpose of the admission was to give the carer a break. In this sense, it may be that the sample consisted of relief care 'success stories'. However, its virtue was that it was not clouded by the inclusion of people whose carer was in hospital because of illness or people who were actually being assessed for their suitability for long term care.

Why has such a conflicting picture emerged? Brodaty and Gresham (1992) suggested five reasons. The first was methodological; studies have gone across users of relief care with different diagnoses and have defined relief care differently. It is also hard to separate any relief effects from those of other services. Second, families may not have become known to services until at a stage when the decision to cease caring may have been made already. Third, carers and arrangers of respite need education not only about the existence of relief care but also the best way to use it. Fourth, relief care is but one type of respite and its necessity will vary according to the needs of the person cared for and the carer. Finally, (in keeping with the medical perspective of the article) the key reason for the failure to demonstrate its efficacy is lack of rigour in its prescription. The authors question whether we can develop a clearer idea of the stage at which relief care should best be offered.

Taking the findings from all these studies into consideration, the literature suggests that this is the service posing most conflict for carers. While it gives them a longer break than that afforded by sitting or day care, the lengthy period of separation means relief care differs intrinsically from either of these services. Furthermore, relief care is a blanket term covering care in diverse settings, at varying frequencies, and for differing purposes. It may be seen as an intermediate service, where the distinctions between community and residential care are most blurred.

Relief care in the study areas

Provision of relief care within the study areas reflected the preponderance of local authority and NHS institutional care noted in the literature.

In Area One, most relief care took place in the NHS. The psychogeriatric service had set aside a ward specifically for relief care and the geriatric service offered places within the assessment wards. Stays usually lasted a fortnight and could be offered as frequently as monthly if requested. The local authority had places in a specialist home for elderly people with mental health problems (EMI) and also in residential care homes. Both officers-in-charge and carers mentioned that elderly people who were very dependent, or had behavioural problems, were offered stays in the EMI home or the NHS. Stays in local authority homes were means tested so the cost to some carers could, on a weekly basis, be equivalent to permanent residential care. The officers-in-charge had differing views as to whether this acted as a disincentive to uptake. Three carers had used a family based respite care scheme organised by the local authority. There were a large number of private residential and nursing homes in the area. Some carers had used these on an occasional basis but not as part of a regular package.

In Area Two, sources of provision were more varied, although the balance of provision rested with local authority homes which all provided some relief care. There was no home dealing specially with residents who had mental health problems in old age, even though some carers and officers-in-charge suggested that one home unofficially seemed to perform this function. All the homes offered day care and so it was possible to introduce relief stays after the elderly person had been for day care at the home. The regularity of stays varied but, on average, amounted to a fortnight's stay every eight weeks. There was a well established family placement scheme in this area, our main source of information on family based respite care. In the NHS, relief care was provided on a psychogeriatric assessment ward. It was also possible to have relief care in the local general hospital. These latter stays were usually arranged by the carer's general practitioner and were restricted to holiday times. While there was a substantial number of private residential care and nursing homes locally, only a few carers had used these for relief stays.

Nearly all the carers in Area Three who had tried relief care used either residential care or EMI homes run by the local authority. This was the area in which relief care was most readily and flexibly available to carers. For instance, in the event of cancelled stays the officer-in-charge would sometimes telephone another carer to offer a break at short notice. Similarly, some homes had what they called 'flexibeds' so that if a carer suddenly became ill or felt she or he needed a break it was possible to arrange for the elderly person to be admitted at very short notice. Relief breaks were charged at a flat rate. There was no family based respite care for elderly people. Within the NHS, relief care came from several sources, an assessment unit which was part of the mental health service, on care of the elderly wards, and in two NHS nursing homes. The two nursing homes preferred to offer relief care as a planned and highly individualised process. First the elderly person would attend the home during the day. Then he or she would try relief breaks. Finally, he or she was permanently cared for in that same home. At the time of the study, there were fewer private homes in Area Three than in the other areas but, even taking this into account, equally small numbers of carers had used residential or nursing homes for relief care.

Use, types and sources of relief care

Fifty eight per cent of the carers had used relief care at least once. In contrast to day care and sitting, this was the one service in which provision did not vary significantly by area. Over 60 per cent of carers had tried relief care in a local authority home and almost 50 per cent had used relief care in the NHS. Eleven per cent of carers had arranged a stay in a residential care or nursing home, the same number as had tried family based respite care.

It is clear from these figures that, as with day care, individual carers could have used more than one source of relief care. However, there *is* a difference in that providers of relief care did not overlap: the elderly people would not use both NHS and local authority provision together. Rather they were used sequentially; as an elderly person became more dependent, he or she might switch from a residential care home to specialist local authority provision for elderly people with mental health problems or the NHS.

There is an additional point worth emphasising. Across the study areas, among the 167 elderly people who had been in relief care, we identified that they had stayed in over 90 different venues! There was a designated respite ward run by the psychogeriatric unit in Area One but, on the whole, nearly all the elderly people stayed in homes alongside permanent residents or on acute sector NHS wards, specialist assessment or continuing care wards for the elderly and so on.

It is evident that there are arguments in favour of integrated relief care, where short stay and permanent residents stay together in one home, and specialised relief care in a designated unit. For instance, there might be positive reasons for choosing a placement with one or two relief care beds but a majority of permanent residents, if the home were geographically convenient for the carer or if it were expected that the elderly person was ultimately likely to move there permanently. Our own discussions with officers-in-charge and the literature on relief care both show that staff working in these settings are familiar with this debate. For the future, it is important that those people planning and commissioning services address the issue of the interface between relief and residential provision and clarify the approach that will be taken in the long term.

Timing and length of relief care breaks

Although we have said that a large percentage of carers had tried relief care, this figure conceals a wide variation in the type and intensity of relief care breaks. Previous work at NISW (Levin *et al.*, 1989) drew attention to the distinction between *regular* relief care, where breaks occurred at fixed intervals with future stays already arranged, and *occasional* relief care where carers usually arranged a stay once a year while they went on holiday. Twenty seven per cent of carers using relief care in this sample had very regular breaks, occurring every six weeks. A similar number had breaks every eight to 12 weeks. Over a year, they might expect to have a service time amounting to seven weeks of relief care. A further 24 per cent used the service occasionally. Only around half of these had a definite date arranged for their next break. Their mean length of service time amounted to just over three weeks per year. The remaining carers were almost equally divided between those who had just begun to try relief care and had experience of only one break at the time of the first interview, and the relief care 'drop-outs', those who had tried relief care once or twice but did not intend to use the service again.

When we examined the lengths of time for which the carers had used relief care we found strong support for the viewpoint expressed by officers-in-charge, social workers, CPNs and psychogeriatricians within the study areas that relief care was a graduated service, tailored to increase in frequency as, in time, the elderly person became more dependent. Those with regular relief care were likely to have been using the service for some time, for over a year in about half the cases. By contrast, most of the occasional users had started the service within the last six months to a year.

We have said that the regularity with which relief care was offered seemed to follow a set pattern, whether this was a break every six weeks, every eight weeks, or once or twice a year while the carer was on holiday. The length of time that each break lasted was even more predictable. Whatever the purpose of the break, wherever the venue, however frequently the carer used the service, the answer to questions on the length of each visit was almost without exception, 'a fortnight'. Some stays lasted a week but frequencies other than these were exceptional.

Relief care as part of a package

Our analyses suggest that the fundamental point of comparison is between packages which do, and those which do not, include relief care. The question of whether day and relief care constitutes a different package to sitting, day and relief care is of secondary importance and says more about the provision of day care and sitting services within each study area than about relief care *per se*.

The need to consider relief care as part of a package is highlighted even further by the fact that just 12 per cent of carers had relief care as their only respite service. Most of this group of carers lived with the elderly person alone and so were even less likely to have someone available with whom they might potentially share their caring responsibilities. It is worth noting that *half* of this admittedly small group would have liked day care or a sitter, suggesting that this was not necessarily the respite arrangement that they would have chosen.

Eight per cent of carers used relief care and sitting. Almost half those with sitting and relief lived in Area One, where there was the largest sitting service, and three of the remaining seven carers paid privately for sitters. Comparisons between carers with sitting and relief care and carers with relief care only must be treated cautiously, given the small numbers involved. Nevertheless, examination of the characteristics of the two groups suggested that there were no significant differences in terms of the elderly people's dependency, the carers' health and so on. This suggests that where the elderly person is unwilling or unable to attend day care, under provision of sitting services can influence packages involving relief care. Fifty three per cent of carers with relief care were also using day care, making this the most frequent combination. This was especially true of carers living in Areas Two and Three. Almost a quarter of carers with relief care used all three respite services. Given that half the carers with this package lived in Area One, it seemed that area was the key factor influencing receipt of this package.

Allocation of relief care

The most important point regarding the allocation of relief care is that any package including relief care was used by elderly people who showed evidence of greater dependency. This is summarised in Table 7.1.

Table 7.1 **Characteristics of the Elderly People by Use of Relief Care**

	% With relief care	% Without relief care	Total (N)	Significance
Mean information and orientation score	4.69	5.99	258	t value 3.03 $p = 0.003$
Mean BRS score	18.89	13.86	279	t value -7.1 $p = 0.000$
Mean number of personal care routines carer helps with	5.75	4.13	287	t value -4.86 $p = 0.000$
Continent	27	73	122	chi-sqr 19.341
Incontinent	53	47	160	$p = 0.0001$
Total	**58**	**42**	**287**	

In our discussion on day care, we found that the characteristics of elderly people attending day centres and day hospitals were essentially very similar. We wondered whether this was also true of elderly people staying in residential and nursing homes, NHS hospitals and in family based respite care placements.

Using the *last* relief care placement as our baseline, this produced what we believe to be one of the most important findings for planning relief care services for elderly people, such as those in our study, in the future. Despite the differing sources of relief care across all the study areas, the most dependent people were *always* cared for in NHS relief care venues. This is shown in Table 7.2 where we compare the mean scores of elderly people in NHS relief care on some of the measures used in the study with those in any other sort of placement.

Table 7.2 Characteristics of the Elderly People by Use of Relief Care Venues

	% With NHS relief care	% With other source of relief care	Total (N)	Significance
Mean information and orientation score	3.54	5.53	146	t value 3.57 p = 0.000
Mean BRS score	20.16	17.91	159	t value 2.53 p = 0.012
Mean number of personal care routines carer helps with	6.51	5.24	163	t value 3.11 p = 0.002
Continent	31	69	73	chi-sqr 5.929
Incontinent	51	49	87	p = 0.0149
Total	**42**	**58**	**287**	

While far fewer people were using family based respite care than local authority homes or the NHS and so we have not shown the figures separately, it is noteworthy that elderly people using family based respite care were least likely to need a great deal of help with their personal care and to show the highest dependency, as indicated on the scores on the CAPE.

Of course, as community care services develop in the future, NHS relief care does not have to be the only option for the sort of elderly people in our sample. What is essential is that there is a recognition that appropriate relief care placements must exist for elderly people whose needs for supervision and help with personal care are extremely high.

The next point to consider was whether any particular carers were more likely to use relief care than others.

Daughters were particularly likely to have used relief care. Among providers of respite, relief care is often seen as a service to be offered if the carer appears to be under great strain and difficulty. In this context, we were not surprised to find a strong relationship between the carers' GHQ scores and use of relief care. Carers who were more likely to consider permanent residential care were also more likely to use relief care. Using the information from the carers' estimate of onset, we found that those who had been caring for some time were much more likely to be using relief care; their mean length of time caring was almost six years, nearly two full years longer than carers without relief care.

If, in general, spouses are less likely to favour using relief care, then under what circumstances will a husband or wife who is a carer agree to the service? We found that by controlling for relationship to the person cared for, among spouses the use of relief care seemed to be accounted for by higher GHQ scores and greater willingness to consider accepting permanent residential care. Thus, for these carers, relief care was a 'last resort' service, a recognition that they were finding it difficult to continue in their caring role.

Table 7.3 Characteristics of the Carers by Use of Relief Care

	% With relief care	% Without relief care	Total (N)	Significance
Relationship to elderly person				
Wife	51	49	96	chi-sqr 29.28
Husband	40	60	70	p = 0.000
Daughter	84	16	62	
Other	64	36	59	
GHQ score from carer's interview				
GHQ 0-5	51	49	173	chi-sqr 9.595
GHQ 6-28	69	31	114	p = 0.002
Accept residential care				
Definitely yes	93	7	30	chi-sqr 37.697
Probably yes	81	19	32	p = 0.000
Probably no	69	31	61	
Definitely no	44	56	154	
Total	**59**	**41**	**287**	

Our conclusions from the allocation of relief care in the study areas suggests that it does not substitute for other community services. Carers and elderly people using relief care form a very different group from those who did not. While there may be exceptions, it is on the whole, a service more suited to those caring for someone in the more advanced stages of Alzheimer's disease.

Carers' reactions to relief care

Almost 80 per cent of carers with relief care said that the stays had made their life better in some way. The most frequently reported benefits were increased patience with the person cared for and feeling more able to deal with caring. One daughter's comment captured the feelings of ambivalence noted in the literature exactly:

I always feel guilty when she goes, then when she's gone I feel free.

Many explained that when they had first tried relief care, they had reached a stage at which some time off from caring had been essential: 'I just knew we needed that break,' said one carer, a viewpoint shared by over 35 per cent of those with relief care. A further 30 per cent felt that, although not quite at that stage, they had certainly been in need of a rest.

The high proportion of carers who saw relief care as useful was not surprising when reviewing whether there was another way a carer might have a longer break. Among the sample *as a whole, not just those with relief care*, only 11 per cent could remember an occasion when relatives or friends had looked after the elderly person for more than 24 hours in the previous year. By contrast, just over 40 per cent of carers mentioned that they had used their last relief break to go away. In fact, the association between whether a carer had had a holiday in the last year and use of relief care almost reached significance. Considering their usual demanding routine, it was impressive that over 20 per cent of carers used relief care to spring clean or decorate. One 74 year old wife, despite her sciatica, explained that she valued relief care because she could:

> ...have a good clean up and my sisters come and we have a good talk.

Returning to the discussion of whether relief care was more suitable for some groups than others, daughters in particular had very positive reactions to relief care. Nearly 40 per cent of daughters with relief care had been using the service for over a year. One explained that:

> It's the breaks you get that help you carry on for longer.

As we shall explain in Chapter Eight, it was certainly true that those carers who had been using relief care for some time were very unlikely to have placed the elderly person in residential care on follow up.

The elderly people's reactions to relief care

Many carers believed that, whereas day care could be seen to be as beneficial to the elderly person as to themselves, this was less true of relief care. Some explained that it was easier to arrange relief breaks if the elderly person did not recognise either their carer or their surroundings :

> [She] didn't quite realise [she was going] - a few years ago it would have been much more difficult.

However, as one husband explained, passive acceptance could also cause distress:

> She just walks off.... that used to hurt me.

In keeping with this picture, only 30 per cent of carers with relief care felt that the elderly person benefited from relief care. This was generally if time had been taken to modify medication or to improve the elderly person's sleeping pattern. A slightly higher proportion felt that the stays made no difference. Ten per cent of carers saw advantages and disadvantages to the stays:

> *She went in by being carried [and] came out walking [but] she cried in there.*

Just over 11 per cent of carers reported a deterioration in the elderly person. A wife reported that her husband had returned:

> *More confused, he didn't know his whereabouts. He slept more. He was more withdrawn.*

Increased confusion was the problem reported most often by carers who had noted a deterioration.

Many elderly people did not remember having been away. On a positive note, one woman who had been going to a particular home for some time, suddenly responded to its name:

> *I like it there, haven't I told you? .... they're very kind.... I go there for a holiday.... We had a Pie and Pea Supper and there was a man singing 'You Made Me Love You' - it's quite a change when you get anything like that.*

Her daughter confirmed that she had indeed arrived to pick up her mother from her last stay and found her enjoying the evening's entertainments.

Improvements to relief care

The Social Services Inspectorate document on short term breaks makes it clear that choice is one of the most important values upon which standards for relief care should be based (SSI, 1993). This gave us one way of structuring carers' suggestions for improvements to relief care.

A number of carers felt that they had not been offered stays frequently enough. Although only 20 per cent of carers with relief care did not have their next break arranged, 40 per cent of this group wanted relief care every four to 12 weeks. Carers on regular programmes were more satisfied with the amount of relief care that had been offered.

Earlier in this chapter we made the point that relief care was nearly always arranged in set slots. This was essential when carers booked holidays or fitted it in around their paid employment (such as the daughter who used the time her mother spent in relief care to put in extra hours at work to enable her to accrue time off in lieu when her mother was at home) but only a very few carers were able to arrange stays at short notice if they felt unable to cope or had suddenly become ill. While rare, an example of how an alternative arrangement did work in practice was given by one woman looking after her husband:

[It's] very variable [and] flexible, they have a dial-a-bed system. I can ring direct to Acorn Villas for a stay of one to four days. For a longer stay I contact the social worker.

Only 36 per cent reported that they had been given a choice in both the timing and length of stay of their relief care breaks. A further 14 per cent said that they had been able to choose the date only. Some carers explained that certain homes only arranged admissions for relief care on set days. Others said that, rather than a fortnight's break, they would have liked a few additional days on their return from holiday to enable them to prepare for the elderly person's return home.

Just 38 per cent of carers had visited the venue for their first relief break in advance. This meant that, for those who had not done so, the opportunity to have their anxieties allayed, build up a relationship with staff and explain the dislikes and preferences of the person cared for was lessened.

Family based respite schemes shone in their matching of family based respite staff with the carers and elderly people using the service. One carer remembered that she had:

...asked for the times I wanted. I met Mrs Collins, she took [mother] for tea and then came here to assess the situation....It was more as if she was going to friends....They vet them [family based respite staff], it's not just anybody.

The time spent preparing carers and elderly people and the close matching of families paid off. Carers who had used family based respite care were much more likely to have rated the care as 'excellent' or 'very good' than other carers. Although only eight per cent of carers overall rated the last relief care venue they had used as providing poor quality care, almost 20 per cent gave a rating of only 'satisfactory'.

While few carers were unhappy with the overall quality of relief care, specific areas were felt to need improvement. A recurrent difficulty was lost clothing and property. Most carers did not seem to have been advised to take preventative measures such as sewing name labels on clothing beforehand. In fact, one husband had returned home so often in the wrong clothes that his wife had built up a special stock of these unsolicited items in which she dressed him each time he was admitted for relief care!

Another complaint made frequently was that the care was often limited. One daughter said:

I've got no gripes but I wish it was more stimulating.

Concerns about standards of care could outweigh carers' preferences for more regular breaks:

> At Hilltop House she [was to] have gone in every six weeks but, you see, the first time she went to Hilltop House it was dreadful...they were short staffed. I didn't consider she was looked after as she should have been so I took Downside Lodge, although it was only [one stay] every ten weeks.

The essence of the carers' comments was that, while the effects of a stay in relief care were not necessarily permanently detrimental, their workload was increased in the short term. For instance, many carers worked hard at promoting the elderly person's continence, but eight per cent of carers with relief care reported that the elderly person had returned home worse. Numerically, this may seem a small number but it could make a tremendous difference on an individual level. Another problem mentioned by a similar proportion of carers was loss of mobility. They complained that, while they made an effort to walk their relative, staff would sometimes use wheelchairs. Considering that most carers were living on their own with the elderly person, if he or she could no longer stand while being washed or dressed, then the carer would have great difficulties.

Some carers also commented on the differing costs of relief care. If the person cared for had stayed in NHS accommodation, no charge was made at the point of delivery. By contrast, at 1991 prices, remembering that some local authority stays were charged at a flat rate or were means tested, others paid an average of just under £50 per week. If the elderly person stayed in a private residential or nursing home, fees could be as much as between £150 and £250 per week. One woman, whose mother's three stays in family placement cost £133 each explained that she had been offered more regular breaks. 'I would like more,' she said, 'but money is a problem'.

Carers who chose not to use relief care

The way in which carers seemed to trade off the benefits and difficulties of relief care is seen best in an examination of the relatively small group, just 10 per cent of those who had tried relief care, which consisted of carers who neither wanted, nor had arranged, another relief stay.

Four of the carers in this group seemed to have based their decision to cease relief care on what they saw as the poor quality of care received. For the rest, (n=11), what seemed to be important was that relief care simply made no difference either to them or their relative. Although they rated the standard of care in the relief care venue as 'good' or 'very good', as one explained:

> *I can manage - besides it was quite a relief when she returned [home] not to have the tedious journey every day to visit.*

Although the differences were not significant, the elderly people in this group were, in overall terms, less dependent and needed less help with their personal care.

Carers without relief care

Almost 60 per cent of those without relief care had never been offered the service. Among those remaining, either the carer or the elderly person had refused the offer. The most frequent reasons for refusal were that it would distress the elderly person, that he or she had 'not reached that stage yet', or that the carer felt able to cope. Above all, however, the desire not to be separated was expressed. One husband stated clearly that:

> *It's a thing I haven't considered, I'd rather go away with her.*

Sadly, we came across only one example where both carer and elderly person had been offered relief care together.

The overwhelming feeling shared by all those who had never used relief care was that they would not want the service. Only 20 per cent of carers without relief care would have wanted it, and of these, the preference was for a one-off break. In addition, aware that the elderly person's condition would deteriorate, a further 20 per cent felt that they might consider it in the future. This was indeed the case. On follow up, almost half of those who had refused it at first interview had started to use relief care.

A number of carers would have wanted family based respite care. Nearly 30 per cent of everyone in the sample thought that it was a good idea. Twenty per cent said that they would definitely like to try it, either then or in the future. There was a small number of carers who felt they would prefer family based relief care to care in a home or hospital. Having said this, there were also carers who believed that staff in homes or hospitals were more experienced and others who were anxious that family based respite staff might not be vetted properly.

Closing issues and summary

Our definition of relief care included any period in which the elderly person spent over 24 hours in any form of residential and nursing care or in a family based respite care scheme. Over 60 per cent of the carers had tried the service at least once, nearly always using local authority homes or NHS hospitals. In fact, relief care was the one respite service in which provision did not vary between the study areas.

The chief value of relief care was the opportunity it gave for carers to have a break lasting more than 24 hours. This was because so few had other family members or friends able to take over the elderly person's care for long periods and alternatives such as holiday schemes for carers and people with dementia are extremely rare. Carers were frequently extremely ambivalent about using relief care, seeing it as necessary for their own wellbeing but feeling guilty for taking the person they cared for from familiar surroundings.

It is important to realise that this was a highly targeted service within which further sub-groups emerged. In some cases, as the elderly person became more dependent and cognitively impaired, relief care was added to an existing package of day care or sitting. This was a gradual process. In others, relief care had been offered in response to the carer's expressions of difficulty. The most dependent elderly people had relief care in the NHS, suggesting that it would be mistaken to assume that this form of relief care merely exists in the absence of alternatives, such as family based respite care or overnight sitting schemes.

The carers' accounts made it clear that improvements could be made to the delivery of relief care. The first problem was that little time seemed to have been spent listening to carers' concerns. It did not seem to be standard practice to pre-arrange visits before the stay took place. Here, family based respite care schemes should be praised for the attention they took to matching carers and families and introducing them to each other. Any initial anxieties about relief care were confirmed or exacerbated if the elderly person returned home with poorer mobility or continence, or if his or her possessions had been lost. The second difficulty was that relief care was often offered in unvarying amounts (a fortnight 'in' and six weeks at home) which may not always have been what the carer preferred.

When considering the impact of relief care as part of a package of respite services, the chief difficulty is its diversity. How does one compare sporadic breaks organised at irregular intervals with pre-planned programmes of stays? Within these limitations, we felt that three overwhelming themes emerged from our results.

The first was that relief care was nearly always only offered to those people whose caring responsibilities were particularly heavy. This group of carers would, as we have seen in Chapter Two, already be more likely to be considering permanent care and to have higher GHQ scores. It is essential to take these factors into account when examining the relationship between the use of relief care and the decision to cease caring.

The second theme relates to the need to ensure that relief care is not offered merely in the absence of other forms of respite provision. It cannot substitute for low levels of day care or sitting. If relief care is nothing more than a 'second best' service then the likelihood of success is reduced because it is not in accordance with the carer's preferences.

The final theme is that while, on the one hand, there was a group of carers who had been using the service for some years, on the other, such programmes will have difficulty in dealing with the needs of those who find the idea of separation too distressing in the first place or those who have already made the decision to cease caring. Therefore, for the service to be most effective, greater clarity is required among care managers and others arranging breaks in identifying which carers will benefit most from relief care and ensuring alternatives exist for others.

8   Outcomes and the Effects of Services

[Life] has been about the same. It's been a bit of a struggle but I can cope.
(Carer of elderly person still at home)

I suppose in a way it [life] is better. I can look back on the happy times and I know she's at peace now.
(Carer of elderly person who had died)

I've had awful emotional upset. At the end of March, it was either her or me who had to go, and I didn't want to put her there.
(Carer of elderly person in a residential home)

Introduction

The preceding chapters have shown that the carers' contribution to successful community care was enormous. At the first interviews, many carers were looking after elderly people whose level of dependency was so high that they met the eligibility criteria for nursing home care; impressively, most carers wanted their relatives to stay at home for as long as possible, even though the strain on some of them was great, and the breaks provided by services and other sources were limited. In this chapter, we move forward to the carers' situation about one year later, showing how many carers, in what circumstances, had realised the aim of continuing to care.

We will tackle two inter-linked sets of questions. These centre on outcomes for the elderly people, in the sense of whether they had died, entered residential care or were still at home, and outcomes for the carers in terms of their mental health. In both instances, we will examine the associations between, on the one hand, the characteristics of the elderly people, the attributes of the carers and the use of the services and, on the other hand, the different outcomes. We will then identify the factors which predict the outcomes most strongly, assessing their relative contributions. Above all, we will address the complex question of whether or not the various services had detectable effects on the outcomes. We are making this question the central concern of this chapter for four reasons.

First, studies which have looked at the impact of community services, counselling and other strategies upon outcomes in the form of admission rates to residential care of people with dementia or upon the mental

[119]

health of their carers have reported only limited effects (Brodaty and Gresham, 1989; Harper *et al.*, 1993; Lieberman and Kramer, 1991; Montgomery and Borgatta, 1989; O'Connor *et al.*, 1991). All have emphasised the potential pitfalls in methodology and interpretation which make it so difficult to unravel the interactions between factors associated with the carer, the person cared for and services.

An additional difficulty has stemmed from a certain sense of over optimism. Commensurate with the scale of the services provided, many studies have reported only moderate successes. Some commentators have taken this to convey that there are no benefits to be had from services (Callahan, 1989). At the other extreme, unrealistic expectations may have been attached to the ability of fairly limited provision to have an appreciable influence in the long term.

Furthermore, the number of evaluative studies is still outweighed by those which are descriptive, even though the services they detail are widely regarded as a strategy to support carers, as recent reviews have shown (Challis, 1992; Moriarty and Levin, 1993a; 1993b; Robbins, 1993).

Fourthly, the recent changes in the organisation and funding of care for very vulnerable people in the UK have fuelled the debate about whether care at home can substitute entirely for care in residential establishments (Challis, 1992). Our results can inform this growing debate by identifying the limits to community care for elderly people with dementia who live with their carers, and by showing that delaying the entry of these elderly people into residential care for as long as possible had consequences for some carers' emotional well-being.

The NISW programme of research is unique among the UK studies published to date because it evaluates a range of ordinary services and combinations of them, rather than a single service or a new intervention, and it covers a relatively large number of service users living in three different localities.

There are four sections to this chapter: in the first section, we report and comment on the outcomes for the elderly people; in the second section, we present the results of a series of statistical analyses which identified the characteristics which best predicted the outcomes for the elderly people; next, we go on to use our qualitative data from the second interviews with the carers to give a picture of their lives in the year between interviews; and finally, we return to present the results of another set of statistical analyses which looked at changes in the carers' mental health between the interviews and its link with the outcomes for the elderly people.

Outcomes for the elderly people

About a year after the first interviews, we followed up all of the 287 elderly people in the sample and found out whether they were still at home, had entered residential care or had died. We interviewed 243 (85 per cent) of the carers again. Of the 44 others, seven could not be traced, 24 could not or did not want to be re-interviewed and sadly, 13 had died. The second interviews concentrated on changes in the elderly people, in their carers, and in the packages of services used and covered the events surrounding an elderly person's move into residential care or death, where appropriate. We took care to recontact the carers systematically so that, as far as possible, the length of time between interviews was similar for each carer and for elderly people in each of the three main outcome groups. This is an important consideration in this sort of sample, where the likelihood of mortality and changes in living arrangements is high. The carers were re-interviewed, on average, 12.7 months later.

Figure 8.1 Outcomes for the Elderly People

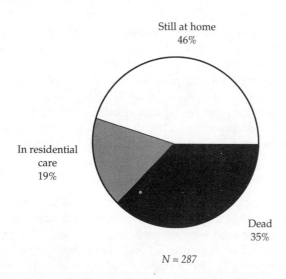

Still at home
46%

In residential
care
19%

Dead
35%

N = 287

As we have stated often, the great majority of the elderly people in this sample were highly or totally dependent. In this context, one of the most important findings of the study was that almost half the elderly people were still cared for at home. These elderly people formed the largest outcome group. Figure 8.1 shows that of the elderly people, 35 per cent had died, 19 per cent had entered residential care and 46 per cent were still at home.

The following findings stand out from the first examination of the outcomes for the elderly people.

Mortality

The proportion of elderly people who had died during the year was high. We were not very surprised by an overall mortality of 35 per cent because we knew from both the NISW studies that, among people with dementia, respite services were targeted on those who were very elderly and formed the most severely dependent and behaviourally disturbed group.

While caution must be exercised when comparing various studies, the evidence from other research suggests that the risk of death for the elderly people in our sample was high. For example, in the Gospel Oak study of all residents aged 65 or over, 13 per cent of them had died three years later, with the likelihood of death increasing with age and a diagnosis of dementia (Cullen *et al.*, 1992). In the Cambridge study of people aged 75 or over with dementia on registers of general practices, 29 per cent died in the first year and 43 per cent had died by the end of the second year (O'Connor *et al.*, 1991). Finally, in the first NISW study of people aged 65 or over with dementia known to general practitioners and a range of other services, 22 per cent overall and 27 per cent of those living with their carers had died one year later (Levin *et al.*, 1989).

The last two studies provide useful benchmarks against which the results of this study can be assessed. The slightly higher overall mortality in our study is likely to be explained by the fact that this is a sample of people with resident carers identified by respite services and therefore contains higher numbers of very elderly disabled people.

Elderly people who had not remained at home

Figure 8.1 shows that the elderly people who were not at home one year later were more likely to have died than to have been in residential care. Almost two-thirds of those who were not at home had died. The carers estimated the time of onset of dementia as, on average, about five years before the first interviews. Thus the majority of these elderly people were looked after for a far longer period by one of their relatives than they were by paid staff in homes and hospitals. Among those who were dead, only a very small number had entered permanent residential care beforehand and most had died in hospital within a few weeks of admission. Typically, therefore, the elderly people had been cared for at home until the last few weeks or months of their life.

Elderly people who remained at home

We find it remarkable that of the elderly people who were still alive, 72 per cent remained at home. This proportion was very similar to the roughly comparable group with resident carers in the first NISW study but it was lower than among the most comparable group in the

Cambridge study, in which the sample was smaller and there were fewer people with severe dementia (Levin *et al.*, 1989; O'Connor *et al.*, 1991). Although we have emphasised that the majority of those who were still alive remained at home, the finding that over a quarter had entered residential care of some sort should not be ignored. It suggests that, even if only for a few months, residential services are required by those whose carers have looked after them willingly over a long period. Therefore, even for elderly people living with dedicated carers, residential services play an important part in the total spectrum of services.

Outcomes for the carers

Twenty one (7 per cent) of the carers had died (n=13) or entered residential care themselves (n=8) about one year later. Of the elderly people that these carers had been looking after, just one was still in the community. He remained there because other relatives had taken over his care when his wife had died. He was one of only four people at home at follow up whose main caring relative had changed between interviews. By contrast, most of those whose carers had died or had become too ill, exhausted or pressurised to continue caring had gone into residential care. This demonstrates starkly the heavy reliance of many elderly people on one particular relative whose availability and ability to care is crucial and hence the fragility of the care network.

Outcomes in the study areas

It was interesting that, overall, there were no significant differences between the study areas in the proportions of elderly people who were still at home, in residential care or dead. Thus elderly people in each of the three study areas were equally likely to have remained at home rather than to have died or entered residential care. Among those who were still alive, the likelihood that an elderly person would have entered residential care did not vary between the areas.

The similarity in the outcomes in the three areas was consistent with the previous NISW study (Levin *et al.*, 1989). This may suggest that whatever the level of provision of residential care, the needs of people with dementia, including those who have carers, for this facility at some stage have to be met somehow. With regard to community services, even though there was variation in the organisation of care management and the mixes of services across the areas, the carers received standard, quite similar and limited amounts of help and time off in each area, and their problems were the same wherever they lived; therefore, it was not unexpected that the elderly people in each area were equally as likely to enter residential care.

Types of residential care

The elderly people who had entered residential care had been placed in NHS hospitals or units, in residential homes run by local authority social services departments and in residential and nursing homes run by the independent sector. Arrangements had been made also for one person to live with another family permanently.

Figure 8.2 Type of Residential Care

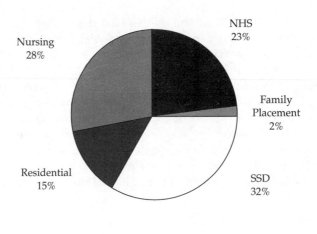

$N = 53$

Figure 8.2 shows that 43 per cent of these elderly people were living in nursing or residential homes run by the independent sector, about one quarter were in NHS hospitals or units for elderly severely mentally infirm people (ESMI) and about one third were in homes run by social services. Most of these elderly people had entered residential care in 1991, that is before the final implementation of the new community care legislation. Therefore, it was interesting to note the extent to which the mixed economy of welfare in the residential care sector was operating before the independent sector was identified as the main provider of residential care for the future.

One finding which seemed important in this context was that the elderly people who had entered NHS hospitals or NHS nursing homes were more severely cognitively impaired and dependent, on average, than those who had entered independent nursing and residential care homes or social services homes. Even though the number of elderly people entering residential care in each of the study areas was too small to draw any firm conclusions, there was some variation between the areas in the type of residential care that they had entered. This balance may reflect differences in the availability of care through the three service sectors at the time and in policy and practice. For example, of the elderly people who were in residential care at follow up, 11 of the 17 in Area One had entered independent sector homes compared with seven of the 17 in Area Two and with five of the 19 in Area Three.

The links with the outcomes

A main theme of this chapter is that there were differences between the elderly people and the carers which were linked to differences in outcomes. It was interesting that the sharpest contrast was between the elderly people who were at home, on the one hand, and those who had died or had entered residential care on the other. Broadly, those still at home were less cognitively impaired, behaviourally disturbed and dependent at the first interviews. Their abilities declined less in subsequent months. Importantly, we shall show in the final section of this chapter that the carers of those still at home showed signs of better mental health, expressed less distress and were far less likely to want permanent residential care at the first interviews than the carers of the others. At follow up, it was the carers who did not have to provide day to day care any longer who showed signs of improvement, on average, in their mental health.

Predicting the outcomes

One of the main advantages of following up the elderly people and their carers was that we could explore the associations between their characteristics at the first interviews and the outcomes one year later. These analyses have provided some interesting answers to two important questions. Firstly, what factors influenced whether an elderly person would be alive or would have died? Secondly, what factors influenced whether an elderly person would be at home or in residential care? Before we present our models of the strongest predictors of these outcomes, we will set out some findings from our initial analyses which showed that there were some key differences at the first interviews between those who subsequently remained at home, entered residential care or died.

The elderly people

Our first analyses revealed that the main characteristic of the elderly people at the first interviews which predicted the outcomes was the level of their cognitive impairment, as measured by the CAPE Information and Orientation Test (Pattie and Gilleard, 1979).

Table 8.1 shows that elderly people who were markedly or severely impaired were less likely to have remained at home than were the others. While we were not surprised by this difference, we noted with interest that it was due mainly to the larger proportions of those who were markedly and severely impaired who had died. We were impressed also by the finding that 44 per cent of elderly people who showed signs of severe dementia were still cared for at home one year later.

Table 8.1 The Scores of the Elderly People on the CAPE Information and Orientation Test by Outcomes

| | Outcomes for the Elderly People | | | | |
	% At Home	% In Care	% Dead	Total (N)	Significance
Information and orientation score					
None, mild, moderate (6-12)	56	17	27	112	chi-sqr 9.4
Marked (3-5)	37	17	46	78	p = 0.049
Severe (0-2)	44	22	34	68	
Total	**47**	**18**	**35**	**258**	
					F = 5.7
Mean score	6.0	4.6	4.6	5.2	p = 0.004
(± 95% CL)	(±0.67)	(±0.94)	(±0.42)	(±0.43)	

It should be noted that the lower the score, the greater the degree of cognitive impairment. The least significant difference (LSD) shows that the mean score of those who remained at home was significantly higher than the mean score of both those admitted to residential care and those who had died.

By contrast with the level of mental impairment, remarkably few of the other characteristics of the elderly people themselves were related to the outcomes for the total sample. Those who had died were older, on average, than those still at home. Overall, however, the gender of the elderly people, their relationship to their carer, the level of their dependency, and the absence or presence of a range of precise problems did not affect outcomes. We began to understand the reasons for the lack of strong associations between the characteristics of the elderly people and the outcomes when we looked at the links between factors in the carers and outcomes.

The carers

We identified two major differences between the carers of the elderly people who remained at home and the carers of those who had entered residential care or had died. These were differences in the carers' mental health and in their attitude towards residential care at the first interviews. As we shall demonstrate, these attributes proved crucial. Overall, other elements such as the carer's relationship to the elderly person, marital status or employment status did not directly affect outcomes. However, poor health in the carers affected the likelihood of entry into residential care but only in the case of elderly people who were cared for by men. For example, of the elderly people who were still alive, 35 per cent of those cared for by men who reported a limiting longstanding illness had entered residential care compared with 13 per cent of those cared for by men who did not report such an illness (p = 0.029); by contrast, the comparable proportions of elderly people entering residential care who were cared for by women with and without such an illness were 33 per cent and 29 per cent respectively. Similar associations were found when we took account of disability in husbands and wives who were caring.

Table 8.2 The Carers' Initial GHQ Scores by Outcomes

| | Outcomes for the Elderly People | | | | |
	% At Home	% In Care	% Dead	Total (N)	Significance
Carers' initial GHQ scores					
GHQ 0-5	55	14	31	173	chi-sqr 13.3
GHQ 6-28	33	24	42	114	p = 0.001
Total	**46**	**19**	**35**	287	
					F = 9.4
Mean score	4.3	8.3	6.6	5.9	p = 0.0001
(± 95% CL)	(±0.85)	(±2.08)	(±1.26)	(±0.718)	

It should be noted that the higher the GHQ score, the higher the likelihood of psychological disturbance. The least significant difference (LSD) shows that the initial GHQ scores of the carers of elderly people who remained at home were significantly lower than the initial GHQ scores of both the carers of elderly people admitted to residential care and those who had died.

Table 8.2 shows that the mean initial General Health Questionnaire (GHQ) scores of the carers of those who had died or had entered residential care were above the cut off point of 5/6 which indicates the probability that they had symptoms of a psychiatric illness such as depression and anxiety (Goldberg, 1978). By contrast, the mean initial GHQ score of the carers of those remaining at home was, at 4.3, below the cut off point. Table 8.2 shows also that over half the elderly people whose carers' GHQ scores were below six, as against one third of those whose carers had higher scores, had remained at home.

We had used both the GHQ and the SELFCARE (D) (Bird *et al.*, 1987), which screens for depression, to assess the carers' mental health and so we were able to examine the associations between the carers' scores on both these self-completed questionnaires and the outcomes. There was a strong association between the carers' initial GHQ and their initial SELFCARE (D) scores. The carers whose GHQ scores were 10 or over were highly likely to show signs of depression on the SELFCARE (D). As would be expected, therefore, there was a relationship between each of these scores and the outcomes. Elderly people whose carers were depressed (SELFCARE (D) scores of six and over) were more likely than others to enter residential care (29 per cent versus 15 per cent) but were equally as likely as the others to have died (35 per cent) ($p = 0.015$).

Taking the evidence from the GHQ and the SELFCARE (D) together, we can be confident that the carers who showed signs of psychological disturbance were more likely to be looking after elderly people who would be placed in residential care or die within a year.

The link between the carers' mental health and the outcomes stood when we took account of many differences between the carers and the elderly people in the sample. For example, first, among the wives and husbands the initial GHQ scores of those whose partner had died or had entered residential care were higher, on average, than the initial GHQ score of those whose partner remained at home a year later. Second, among the elderly people who were incontinent or who disturbed their carers during the night, those whose carers had higher initial GHQ scores were less likely to have remained at home.

Even though the carers' mental health was important, it was their attitude towards residential care at the first interviews which predicted the outcomes most strongly.

Table 8.3 The Attitudes of the Carers to Residential Care by Outcomes

| | Outcomes for the Elderly People | | | | |
	% At Home	% In Care	% Dead	Total (N)	Significance
Carer would accept residential care					
Yes	14	39	47	62	chi-sqr 42
No	56	11	33	215	$p = 0.000$
Total	47	17	36	277	

Table 8.3 shows that elderly people whose carers would definitely or probably have accepted residential care were very unlikely to be at home a year later. Eighty six per cent of the elderly people in this group had entered residential care or had died. By contrast, less than half the elderly people whose carers would definitely or probably not have accepted residential care had been placed there or had died. It was

striking that of the 30 elderly people whose carers definitely wanted residential care, only one was still at home, and over half were in long term care a year later; of the 154 elderly people whose carers definitely did not want residential care, over half were still at home and only 14 per cent were in long term care.

The strong association between the carers' attitude to residential care at the first interviews and outcomes for the elderly people was demonstrated also by the proportion of elderly people in each of the outcome groups whose carers would have accepted residential care. Seven per cent of the carers of elderly people who had remained at home would have accepted residential care, compared with 50 per cent of the carers of those who were in residential care and 29 per cent of the carers of those who had died ($p= 0.000$).

In summary, our first analyses showed that the level of cognitive impairment in the elderly people, the carer's mental health and their attitude towards residential care predicted whether an elderly person had remained at home, had entered residential care or had died a year later. We have shown in earlier chapters, however, that the elderly people who were very dependent, whose carers had a high number of symptoms of psychological distress and who would have accepted residential care were more likely to have used two or three respite services, one of which was relief care, usually combined with day care. Therefore, in our preliminary analyses we looked for links between the services that they had used at the first interviews and the outcomes.

The services

When we looked for the first time at the effects of services on outcomes for the elderly people, the following findings stood out.

Firstly, the number, the type and the particular combination of respite services used at the first interviews were associated with the residential outcomes but they were not associated with death.

Secondly, Table 8.4 shows that the outcomes for elderly people who used only community based respite services were different from the outcomes for those who used either community based and residential respite services or only residential respite.

This result confirms that it is indeed useful to divide the users of day care and sitting services into two groups on the basis of whether they use residential respite, a distinction which we have made repeatedly in the preceding chapters. Thus it would have been wrong to conclude that the use of day care or sitting services was not associated with the outcomes because on the surface the groups using these services were as likely as those not using them to have remained at home, entered residential care or died. A very different picture emerged when we took account of whether these elderly people had entered relief care.

Table 8.4 Type of Respite Services Used at First Interview by Outcomes

| | Outcomes for the Elderly People | | | Significance |
	% At Home	% In Care	Total (N)	
Type of respite services				
None	74	26	*31*	
Day and/or sitting without relief care	86	14	*50*	chi-sqr 8.3 $p = 0.016$
Relief care with or without day, sitting	64	36	*105*	
Total	**72**	**28**	*186*	
Mean no. of services	1.45	1.68	1.55	$t = 1.53$
(± 95% CL)	(±0.16)	(±0.26)	(±0.13)	$p = 0.07$

We found that the elderly people who had day care or sitters but did not have residential relief care were more likely to have remained at home. By contrast, the elderly people who had residential relief care, which was almost always used in conjunction with day care or sitting, were most likely to have entered residential care. This finding was expected because relief care was targeted primarily on highly or totally dependent elderly people, it occupied an intermediate position in the service continuum between domiciliary and day care services at one end and long term residential care at the other, and the earlier NISW study had shown that elderly people with relief care were more likely to have entered residential care (Levin *et al.*, 1989).

Although elderly people with relief care were more dependent, on average, than others, we recognised that in each dependency category there were some elderly people who entered relief care and others who did not, a difference which arose partly because daughters were less reluctant to use the service than wives and husbands. We looked therefore for the apparent effect of relief care on residential outcomes for people with different levels of dependency, taking account of their carers' GHQ scores and attitudes towards residential care. There were constraints on these analyses because of the small numbers of those still alive who had entered residential care (36 per cent with relief care and 18 per cent without it). Broadly, we found that at each level of dependency the carers who used relief care manifested more symptoms of psychological strain and were more likely to want permanent residential care than those who did not use relief care. Impressively, of the elderly people in the maximum dependency group, 19 out of 20 of those who had not entered relief care remained at home a year later, compared with 33 out of 56 (59 per cent) of those who had entered relief care. Again the differences between these two groups which related to the carers' mental health and attitudes to residential care suggested that the carers with relief care were reaching the limits of their capacity to care.

The way in which a relatively intensive package of respite was a precursor to placement in residential care was highlighted by the finding that of the elderly people with day care, those who attended at least four days a week were more likely to have entered residential care than those who attended less often. Most elderly people who went to day care more than three times a week used relief care also, were very dependent and had carers who were psychologically distressed. They formed, therefore, a very vulnerable group on the margins of residential care at the first interviews. Nevertheless, of those with day care at least four times a week and of those with relief care at the first interviews who were still alive a year later, two-thirds had remained at home. Furthermore, elderly people who had used relief care were not any more likely than others to have died. This result adds to the growing literature showing that residential relief care does not affect mortality, as reviewed by Brodaty and Gresham (1992).

Thirdly, when we considered the other community services used by the elderly people and the carers with and without respite, home help was the only service which was associated with different outcomes.

Table 8.5 Use of the Home Help Service at First Interview by Outcomes

| | Outcomes for the Elderly People | | | | |
	% At Home	% In Care	% Dead	Total (N)	Significance
Home help					
Yes	35	28	37	75	chi-sqr 8.6
No	51	15	34	211	$p = 0.014$
Total	**47**	**18**	**35**	**286**	

Elderly people whose carers were assisted by the home help service were more likely to have entered residential care than others, as Table 8.5 shows. Although this difference may seem curious initially, it is understandable when the characteristics of the carers allocated the home help service at the first interviews are taken into account. The carers receiving home help services were far more likely than others to be wives and husbands aged 75 and over and, relatedly, to have disabilities themselves, especially if they were women. Thus the carers' health was a common reason for using home help services, as well as respite services. This package played a vital part in enabling very elderly and disabled carers to look after their partners at home for as long as possible, as the great majority wanted to do. It could not prevent an elderly person's admission to residential care once their carers' health had broken down. Sadly, the carers using home help services were more likely to have entered residential care themselves or to have died a year later, events which precipitated their relatives' placement in residential care.

Fourthly, our study provided fresh evidence that respite services are offered for very different reasons. After they had accepted day or relief care, some carers had continued looking after their elderly relative for a much longer period than others. Table 8.6 shows that of the elderly people with day care, those who had attended for between five months and a year before the first interviews were more likely to have entered residential care. Strikingly, of the elderly people who were still alive, 46 per cent of those attending day care for between five and twelve months were in residential care, compared with only 26 per cent of those attending for a shorter period and only 18 per cent of those attending for more than a year. A similar contrast was found among those with sitters but the finding was not significant at the five per cent level.

Table 8.6 Months Using Day Care at First Interview by Outcomes

| | Outcomes for the Elderly People | | | | Significance |
	% At Home	% In Care	% Dead	Total (N)	
Months using day care					
Under 5 months	46	16	38	57	chi-sqr 10.8 $p = 0.03$
5 - 12 months	33	28	39	61	
Over 12 months	59	13	28	71	
Total	**47**	**18**	**35**	**189**	
					F = 2.382
Mean no. of months ($\pm$ 95% CL)	18.87 ($\pm$4.3)	12.49 ($\pm$4.14)	13.74 ($\pm$4.05)	15.9 ($\pm$2.56)	$p = 0.095$
T-test for Home vs in care	18.87	12.49			t value 2.15 $p = 0.03$

Relief care is usually offered after an elderly person has become used to day care, and husbands and wives only accept it when the strains of caring become very great. In the case of relief care, among the elderly people alive at follow up, the main difference was in outcomes for those who had used the service for less than a year before the first interviews, 38 per cent of whom had entered residential care, compared with only 11 per cent of those using the service for at least a year.

It seems, therefore, that some carers found day and relief care very appropriate and acceptable, using them to secure a much needed break from the relentless task of caring. Others appeared to have been offered day and relief care when their capacity to continue to care was reaching its limits and residential care would have to be arranged in the near future. The apparent value of the number of months using day and relief care in distinguishing for those groups who were likely to enter residential care, which we found in our study, was consistent with the findings of Gilleard (1987). His influential study of patients attending psychogeriatric day hospitals also showed that carers were less likely to have placed an elderly person in residential care if they had used the service for several months.

Taken together, the findings from our first examination of the factors influencing the outcomes for the elderly people showed that the level of cognitive impairment in the elderly people, their carer's mental health and attitude to residential care, their use of relief care and home help services and the length of time that they had used the two main respite services were important considerations. We showed in earlier chapters, however, that many of these elements were interlinked. Therefore, we undertook a series of multivariate analyses to tease out as far as possible which characteristics of the elderly people influenced whether they had died or were still alive at follow up, and which attributes and problems were the strongest predictors of residential outcomes for those who were still alive at follow up.

Who had died and who was still alive?

The first analyses suggested that the elderly people who were more likely to have died in the year after the first interviews were those who were older, on average, those who were more severely cognitively impaired, and those who had diagnosed health problems especially strokes and heart disease. In consequence, elderly people who required help with most personal care routines, those who were incontinent, those who had tried to hit their carers and those whose carers had the least leisure time at the first interviews were more likely to have died.

Figure 8.3 shows the results of a logistic regression analysis which was undertaken to quantify the contribution of the various characteristics of the elderly people to the outcomes 'alive or dead'. The figure shows that mortality was associated with the level of cognitive impairment in the elderly people, as measured by their scores on the CAPE Information and Orientation Test, with their age and gender, and with whether they had suffered a stroke. Other variables which were tested in the model included the level of the elderly people's dependency, as measured by their total score and scores on the subsections of the Behavioural Rating Scale of the CAPE, the

**Figure 8.3 Logistic Regression Parameters for the Risk of Death for the Elderly Person
(EP) between First Interview and Follow Up**

Constant only in the model   -2 Log Likelihood = 325.2   df = 253
Full model   -2 Log Likelihood = 290.0   df = 248

Variable	Scale	B	Wald	df	Significance	Exp(B)
Age of EP	(58-98)	0.0675	10.7	1	0.0011	1.07
Stroke	(0,1)	0.8385	7.3	1	0.0069	2.31
Sex of EP	(0,1)	0.8417	7.2	1	0.0070	2.32
Memory	(0-12)	-0.1188	6.5	1	0.01	0.89
Constant		-6.617				

The Wald statistic gives an indication of the relative importance of each variable increasing the likelihood of death. The calculated coefficients [Exp(B)] are the multiplication factors associated with the death odds ratio of every unit increase in the independent variable. For example, the death odds ratio is 2.32 times greater for men compared to women after allowing for the other factors. For every unit increase in the information and orientation score (memory), the odds ratio for death declines by a factor of 0.89.

number of personal care routines that the elderly people were helped with, whether they had hit their carers, the length of time since onset of symptoms of dementia and the area in which they lived. We found, however, that these factors did not influence the outcome when we controlled for them in the analysis.

It is difficult, of course, to predict mortality on the basis of information about an elderly person one year earlier. Our model is able to explain only 15 per cent of the variance in mortality. Nonetheless, it seemed to us to be worth reporting as it indicates the relative importance of the variables which significantly affected the mortality of the elderly person. It shows that in a sample of people with dementia the likelihood of death increased with the severity of cognitive impairment and age; it shows also that men were more likely to have died than women and that those who had suffered a stroke before the first interview were more likely to have died. In a later section of this chapter, we will describe how the carers of elderly people who had died reported more deterioration in their relatives' health and abilities after the first interviews, confirming that death came suddenly for some people and was a long, drawn out process for others.

Predicting residential outcomes

Background

In this section we move on to the elderly people who were still alive at the follow up and make comparisons between those who remained at home and those who had been admitted to any type of residential care.

We shall present a statistical model of the factors in the carers and the elderly people in this sample which best predict the residential outcomes, quantifying their relative contributions.

We consider that the strong influence of the carers on these outcomes over the time span of a year is one of the most important findings of our study, contributing as it does to the understanding of the factors which precipitate the admission into residential care of some of the most dependent elderly people who have been cared for at home.

When interpreting our data, it is essential to remember that our sample was composed of elderly people with cognitive impairment who lived with their carers and who were using respite services or had contact with the professionals who assess for these services. Our results must be seen, therefore, in the context of other studies which have shown that people with dementia are far more likely than others to enter residential care, that, at each level of disability, those who live alone are more likely to be admitted, and that, in general the proportion of all people with dementia who live in residential care increases with the severity of the degree of dementia (Brodaty and Gresham, 1992; Gilleard, 1992; Levin *et al.*, 1989; Sinclair *et al.*, 1990).

Most recently, Opit and Pahl (1993) have re-analysed the Disability Survey carried out by the Office of Population Censuses and Surveys (OPCS, 1988) to produce estimates of the relative and absolute risk of admission to residential care among people aged 75 and over and to develop a valuable model which can be used by those responsible for planning and purchasing services to estimate the number of elderly people in a given population who are likely to enter residential care in any one year. Importantly, Opit and Pahl (1993) confirm the greatly increased likelihood of admission to residential care among elderly people with dementia and the key contribution of carers who live with people with dementia to the maintenance of the most dependent people in this group at home. The information from the NISW Respite Care study shows that there is potential to build on the model provided by Opit and Pahl (1993) through the use of more detailed information on particular groups of elderly people and on their carers, subject to the caveat that it calculates the risk factors for admission only for a sample of people with dementia who live with their carers and are known to services.

The NISW model

In developing a model of the factors determining whether an elderly person remained at home or entered residential care, we looked at three areas: the first was the characteristics of the elderly people; the second was the characteristics of their carers; and the third was their use of day, sitting, relief care and the other community services. The preliminary analyses suggested that there were some marked differences at the first interviews between the elderly people who remained at home and those admitted to residential care one year later, as we showed earlier in this chapter. Thus, there was an increased likelihood of admission among the elderly people who were more severely cognitively impaired, whose carers were psychologically distressed, whose carers would have accepted long term residential care and among those who used home help services and residential relief care. As we have stated, most of these variables are strongly inter-related. In order to take account of the interactions between them, and also to treat each of these variables separately, we undertook a series of multivariate analyses.

These analyses yielded a model of the best combination of factors in the elderly people and their carers which between them predicted whether an elderly person remained at home or entered residential care. The use of linear regression and logistic regression techniques produced the same results.

Figure 8.4 confirms that the carer's attitude towards residential care for their elderly relative at the first interviews predicted the outcomes on its own and was the most influential of all the predictors of residential outcomes considered for the model. As would be expected, it was the elderly people whose carers would not have accepted residential care who were more likely to have remained at home. By comparison, those whose carers would have accepted residential care were twice as likely as the others to have been placed in long term care during the next twelve months.

Figure 8.4 shows also that the level of an elderly person's cognitive disability influenced the outcome, albeit to a lesser extent than their carer's attitude towards long term care. The likelihood of admission to care increased with the severity of cognitive impairment, as reflected in the elderly person's score on the CAPE Information and Orientation Test. As shown also, the ability or inability of an elderly person to understand what the carer communicated to them by speaking, writing or gesturing and to communicate themselves in any manner, as reflected in their scores on the relevant subsection (CDS) of the CAPE Behaviour Rating Scale, influenced residential outcomes in the expected direction, and so, too, did their total dependency score on the Behaviour Rating Scale of the CAPE. In addition, the age of the elderly person made a relatively small but significant contribution to residential outcomes in that the likelihood of admission increased with age.

Finally, the model shows that the carers' mental health, as measured by their GHQ scores, made a contribution to the outcome. Again, the higher the number of symptoms suggestive of depression and anxiety in the carer, the greater the likelihood of placement in residential care.

This model suggests that whether an elderly person was at home or in residential care a year later was a product of four factors. Two of these

Figure 8.4 The Factors Determining whether an Elderly Person Remained at Home or Entered Residential Care.

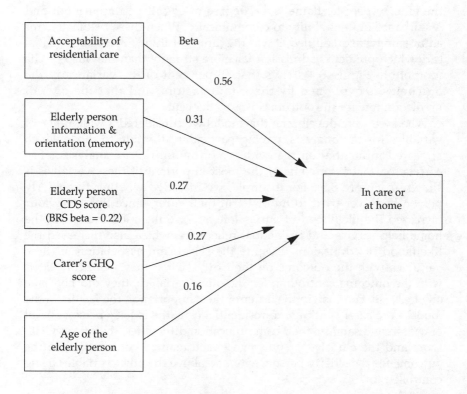

	Predicted	Actual	% correct
At home	108	114	95%
In Care	27	38	71%
Total			89% (n = 152)

The flow diagram illustrates the best fit model using a logistic regression. Four outliers and the 101 elderly people who were dead at follow up are excluded. The linear regression produced the same result, so the standardised beta coefficients in the diagram are quoted from this. These coefficients give an indication of the relative importance of each of the variables in predicting the outcome for the elderly person. The adjusted R-Sqr, or the variance explained by the model, is 53%, with an overall prediction rate of 89%.

factors were attributes of the carers, namely their attitude towards residential care and their mental health. The other two were factors in the elderly people, namely the degree of cognitive impairment and disturbance in their ability to communicate. When these risk factors for admission were quantified, it was the carer's attitude towards residential care which predicted admission far more strongly than the others. The footnote to Figure 8.4 shows that 53 per cent of the variance in the outcomes is explained by these four factors, and that the overall prediction rate for the outcomes was 89 per cent.

When we were developing this model we considered a wide range of variables for the analysis, paying particular attention to those which appeared influential on the evidence of the univariate analyses. The correlation matrix of some of the most important of these variables is shown in Figure 8.5. For example, we included whether the elderly person had ever tried to hit or harm their carer, since this behaviour increased the likelihood of admission, and we included the use of the home help service and residential relief care, which also increased the likelihood of admission. Despite the significant association of these variables with the outcome on their own, when they were correlated with the outcome controlling for the other variables, they did not have an effect. By contrast, in the order of their importance, the factors in the model - the carer's attitude to residential care, the elderly person's level of cognitive disability, their communication difficulties, the carer's GHQ score and the elderly person's age - each made a contribution to the outcome for the elderly person, over and above the other variables being controlled for.

Figure 8.5 The Correlation Matrix for Some of the Key Variables Considered in the Predictive Model

Pearson correlations:	In care	Accept	GHQ	Physical disability	Memory	BRS score	Hit by EP	Age of EP	Respite care
In care	1.00								
Carer:									
Accept	0.53**	1.00							
GHQ	0.33**	0.33**	1.00						
Phys. disability	0.12	0.09	0.25**	1.00					
Elderly person:									
Memory	-0.14	0.05	0.07	0.12	1.00				
BRS score	0.10	0.21*	0.18*	0.00	-0.39**	1.00			
Hit by EP	0.19*	0.20**	0.24**	0.08	-0.27**	0.33**	1.00		
Age	0.01	0.12	0.11	0.04	-0.01	0.04	0.01	1.00	
Services:									
Respite care	0.21*	0.36**	0.23**	0.00	-0.11	0.33**	0.24**	0.17	1.00
Home help	0.23*	0.15	0.19*	0.35**	0.06	-0.09	0.06	0.07	0.11

N of cases : 172   1-tailed Significance : * 0.01 **0.001

In concluding this section, we shall locate our results in the context of other research and draw out their implications for policy and practice.

Firstly, our research adds to the growing body of evidence suggesting that the attributes and attitudes of the carers are the most influential predictors of outcomes for samples of highly dependent people, especially those with dementia (Gilleard, 1984; Morris *et al.*, 1988; Levin *et al.*, 1989; Lieberman and Kramer, 1991; Brodaty and Gresham, 1992; Jones and Salvage, 1992). Carers who live with the person whom they look after meet the needs of the most dependent people in the community, many of whom meet the criteria of eligibility for residential care. The great majority of these carers want to look after their relatives themselves and manage to do so for as long as possible. It seems crucial, therefore, to support these carers and attempt to alleviate their problems. However, when, as in the case of our sample, the elderly people become increasingly cognitively impaired, the carers show signs of great strain and come to the conclusion that they have reached the limits of their caring capacity, it is likely that residential care will be required. The simple question, 'would you accept residential care for [your relative] if offered now?' provides the best indicator of what happens in the following year. Its use by practitioners responsible for assessment may enable the services to plan residential admissions and target community services.

Secondly, it was interesting that the use of residential respite care and the home help service did not increase the likelihood of entry into residential care, when factors in the elderly people and in the carers were taken into account. Elderly people with relief care were very unlikely to have entered residential care if their carers would not have accepted it at the first interview, and very likely to have entered it if their carers would have accepted it. This suggests that relief care may serve two purposes: it can assist determined carers over a long period, making their task more manageable, and it prepares the elderly people and their carers for separation when the severity of disability in the former and the strain in the latter become so great that residential care can no longer be avoided. If this is so, relief care plays a major part in the support of carers coping with severe dependency and should surely be available to such carers if they want it.

Thirdly, we emphasise that the model we have presented deals with the characteristics and problems faced by the carers at the first interview. The progressive nature of dementia should be recognised, as should the importance of the carers' health. As we shall show in the next section, events after the first interviews also affected the outcomes. The decrease in an elderly person's abilities and hence the increase in their level of dependency was greater, on average, among those who entered residential care or died subsequently than among those who remained at home.

Furthermore, as we have stated earlier, the death of a carer, or their entry into residential care themselves after the first interviews, strongly influenced residential outcomes for the elderly people. Though they were a very small group, only one of the surviving elderly people whose carers had died or been admitted to residential care remained at home at the follow up. To put this point another way, about one quarter of the elderly people in residential care had carers who had died or were in care themselves at the follow up. The correlations between the outcomes for the carers and the elderly people explain in part the better prediction rate of our model for those still at home than for those entering residential care. The effect of the loss or absence of a carer on outcomes is consistent with the results of Opit and Pahl's study (1993) which showed that this occurrence was one of the risk factors for admission to residential care.

The 243 carers who were interviewed twice provided vivid accounts of their experiences in the intervening period, which highlighted the gradual deterioration of the elderly people's abilities, increasing strain in many carers and the relationship of these elements to the outcomes, as described under the next headings.

Changes in the elderly people after the first interviews

At their second interview, the carers were asked about the elderly people's abilities and behaviours and whether these had changed. In addition, they completed the Behaviour Rating Scale of the CAPE again, which enabled us also to assess changes in dependency levels by calculating the differences between the initial and follow up BRS scores. We looked at the changes in the elderly people which occurred in the months after the first interview that they were looked after by their carers at home. Of course, for the elderly people who remained at home, this was the month of the carer's second interview. For those who had entered residential care or had died, the last month at home was literally the last month that they had been looked after by their carers before they had been admitted to a hospital or a residential home or in a few cases had died at home. In the case of 25 elderly people whose carers were re-interviewed, the last month that they had lived at home was the month that their carers were first interviewed and so the questions on changes were not asked at the second interviews.

The chronic and progressive nature of dementing illness was highlighted by the changes in the elderly people between the first interviews and their last month at home. Sadly, the carers reported deterioration in the mental abilities of eight in ten elderly people, in the physical health of six in ten of them, and in the behaviours of half of them. Almost all the elderly people who had not deteriorated in these respects were said to be 'the same' at both interviews, rather than 'better' or 'better in some ways and worse in others'. The 'same' group included those whose abilities at first interview were so severely impaired that they already required maximum assistance.

The carers of elderly people who were at home, in residential care or had died were equally likely to report deterioration in the elderly people's mental abilities. Unsurprisingly, those whose relatives had died were more likely than others to report deterioration in the elderly people's physical health between first interview and the last month at home, and those whose relatives were at home were least likely to report changes for the worse in the elderly people's behaviours during this period. This deterioration was only to be expected, given the extreme old age of many elderly people in the sample and the progressive nature of dementia. It had implications, however, not only for the elderly people but also for their carers and for services.

First, increased physical and mental disability and behavioural disturbance in the elderly people had resulted in the majority of carers having to provide increased help with personal care. Second, a key question was whether services had the sensitivity and capacity to increase their input as the elderly people deteriorated, and if so, whether they could cushion the impact upon the carers of their relatives' increasing need for care.

Some elderly people in each of the three outcome groups had deteriorated to the point of very severe dependency in the last month at home, a condition typically summed up by the carers as, 'I have (had) to do everything for her'. Mr Salkeld, describing his wife's condition prior to admission to hospital, said:

She didn't even realise that she should swallow the food put into her mouth.

Mr Bach, still looking after his wife, explained:

Her memory is getting worse. She doesn't know who I am or who her children are .... She's getting further and further away from life .... It's getting more difficult. I have to dress and undress her, and dry her after a shower.

Encouragingly, the comments of some carers pointed to the way in which a new or more frequent service had helped them to tolerate increased dependency. Mrs Seales, for example, explained:

In some ways it's much worse because night-time is difficult but day care has helped.

And Mrs Angus said:

He has got more dependent and I get very tired but we now have regular respite which keeps me going.

However, the limitations of services were also pinpointed by some carers' comments. For example, one carer whose wife had died, explained:

> *The last year was the worst. It got harder and harder and she was very incontinent. She needed much more looking after and I couldn't get nurses on Saturdays or Bank Holidays. I had to wash her and everything .... She fell down several times.*

The carers' accounts of the deterioration in the elderly people's abilities were corroborated when we compared the elderly people's initial scores on the CAPE Behaviour Rating Scale (BRS) with their follow up BRS scores which measured their level of dependency in their last month at home.

Among the 218 elderly people for whom the BRS was completed twice, the mean BRS score rose from 16.55 to 18.73, a mean increase of 2.18. Although the change for the total sample was small, it reflected increasing dependency. In further analyses we examined the links between the change in BRS scores and the different outcomes for the elderly people, controlling for their initial BRS scores. These analyses showed that there was a mean increase in the BRS scores of the elderly people in each of the outcome groups. As one would expect, the increase in dependency whilst at home was greater among the elderly people who had been placed in residential care and those who had died than among those who had remained at home. The mean increase in BRS dependency scores was 1.55 for those still at home compared with 3.06 for those in residential care and with 2.92 for those who had died, a difference between those at home and the other two groups which was significant at the five per cent level ($F = 4.32$, $p = 0.01$).

As well as highlighting the progressive nature of dementia, the sharper increase in dependency and its consequences for the carers among those who had not remained at home supplemented the analyses which showed that scores on the CAPE at the first interviews predicted the outcomes, as we have reported earlier.

The carers' experiences

The year between interviews had been difficult for most carers, and only one quarter of them described their lives as unchanged at the end of it. In many respects, their experiences were shaped by what had happened to their elderly relatives.

Carers of elderly people who died or entered residential care

Clearly, a major outcome for the carers, which followed from outcome for the elderly people, was whether they remained carers or whether they were now ex-carers, as those no longer looking after someone everyday have come to be called. This shift had taken place for half the carers in the sample. These carers had lived through a period of enormous change, and their lives were very different from before. Each carer was unique, and some had experienced their relative's death or move into residential care more recently than others: they came to terms with separation and loss at different paces and, for many reasons, their reactions to similar experiences varied. Thus, a life without the responsibilities of caring was perceived as better by some, worse by others and both better and worse by yet others. Nonetheless, these ex-carers' accounts highlighted the many consequences of no longer having to care. For example, there were adjustments to be made to living alone, to having less money, to having less work, and to feeling less tired; and there were more opportunities to go out and to spend time on one's own interests.

As would be expected, more of the carers whose relatives had died had reservations about these changes compared with those whose relatives had gone into care. Of those whose relatives had died, one third considered that, in general, their lives were better, one third considered that their lives were worse, and the rest took the view that their lives were better in some ways and worse in others. Almost all were thankful that their relatives were released from suffering, and most were relieved that they no longer had the work and worry of caring. However, the majority were still sad about their relative's death and they missed them. For example, Mr Fowles looked so much better when the interviewer visited him again that she barely recognised him. He confirmed that his health had improved because he was more relaxed now but said passionately of his wife:

I miss her like blazes especially at night. We used to sleep in each other's arms. After tea, it always hits me that she's not here.

Mrs Luckett had taken her husband's death very badly. Depressed on the evidence of her second SELFCARE (D) and GHQ scores, she explained:

I feel worse now than when he first died. I miss looking after my husband. I still can't get over it.

This woman, like half the carers with more leisure time, had mixed feelings about having more time to herself. She said:

I've got more freedom now. I can make appointments and see people when I wish. In some ways, it's a change for the best but not under the circumstances. I didn't have time to be lonely before.

Also Mrs Luckett was one of the two-thirds of carers whose relative's death had left them with a reduced income. She commented:

> *I've lost his major pension and Attendance Allowance. It's a struggle to pay for everything. I have to count every penny ...*

Treatment by public services at the time of bereavement was not always as considerate as it might have been. One wife, whose husband had developed Alzheimer's disease some four years previously, had not been told about Attendance Allowance until he had entered residential care. At the suggestion of the person in charge, she submitted a backdated claim. In the meantime, while her application was being processed, her husband died. She and her daughter had tears in their eyes as they recounted receiving a letter suggesting that, as her husband was now dead, she might want to consider withdrawing her claim. Policies towards following up carers who had been bereaved varied, and so some professionals visited and others did not. The withdrawal of services following bereavement was keenly felt by carers who were isolated. As one man explained:

> *As soon as my wife passed away, everything stopped. I didn't see anyone.*

Some of the carers whose relatives had entered residential care commented that they would have liked some professional counsel during the transition into care. The decision to accept residential care had been a major one, often only taken because the elderly people had become severely dependent or difficult or because the carers were exhausted or ill themselves. For example, Mrs Gaunt explained that she did not like the idea of her husband going into hospital care but that she had had to accept it because she could no longer manage him:

> *He was getting bad tempered and knocking me about. At first, they thought they might be able to calm him down but he got worse.*

And a 70 year old daughter caring for her 90 year old mother with no help from services explained:

> *I was working 24 hours a day looking after my mother. She was incontinent and waking me at nights. If she hadn't gone into the home, I would have had a nervous breakdown.*

Although lonely, this daughter said that her life was better because:

> *I have not got the strain. I'm sleeping better. I visit her twice a week and I still feel upset. She can't communicate .... She was a good mother.*

Overall, the carers who had accepted residential care were more likely to say that their lives were better than those whose relatives had died. Of those with residential care, almost half said that their lives were better, one quarter said that their lives were worse, and most of the others were ambivalent. In general, those who favoured residential care at first interview seemed happier about obtaining it than the others. Understandably, after many years together, few elderly spouses accepted separation easily, and some were wearing themselves out visiting daily. No longer exhausted by caring and, therefore, unable to sleep at night, one husband did not relish his increased freedom. He explained:

> *The things I used to enjoy don't attract me as much now. All I can do is keep the place tidy. I have the whole evening to myself now. It seems all wrong. When you cut out looking after someone 24 hours a day, its all topsy turvy.*

However, most carers talked positively about beginning to build up their social lives again, and about enjoying simple pleasures such as playing the piano, walking the dog, going to bingo and re-joining a club. Although broken hearted when her husband went into a home and lonely since, Mrs O'Shea said:

> *I'm only just beginning to find myself. It's like being born again. I'm no longer a cog in a machine that never stops .... I went to a lecture at the hospital the other day.*

Only one third of the carers had initiated the move to residential care themselves. Most of the others had been offered the option by a doctor, a social worker or a nurse, who had observed deterioration in the elderly person, and exhaustion in the carer. These professionals seemed to have recognised that community care could no longer be maintained without placing intolerable strain on the primary carers. For example, a young daughter-in-law with many family commitments said that she would have 'cracked up' without the community psychiatric nurse who had helped her to decide on residential care. For those carers who had not wanted residential care, the question remains whether other types and increased quantities of services might have enabled them to continue to care. The social worker for one husband, who hated being separated from his wife, might have made attempts to help this man find a private sitter. Our interviewer wrote:

> *Day and relief care not wanted but sitters wanted but not available in that area.*

A daughter, whose day care had increased from one to two days, speculated:

I might have been able to carry on if she'd been able to go five days.

Most carers visited their relatives in the residential home or hospital every week and seemed satisfied with the care provided. However, some certainly had reservations about it which should be taken seriously. One daughter said:

> *I think the system lets you down ... There is just not enough stimulation in the old people's homes. The staff are not trained and they need to get their act together. They do not treat the old people as though they are worth something.*

Mr Creasey was in a good position to comment as he lived with his wife in a home where he paid £21,000 a year for their care. His opinion was:

> *We're well looked after and get nice meals. People are kind if you do as you are told.*

Another carer had no doubt about the service which was most helpful to her. Her advice to others in her position was:

> *Get residential care before you get desperate.*

Carers of elderly people remaining at home

The carers whose relatives remained at home also had plenty to say at second interview about what they liked and disliked about the various services. Half these carers said that their life was much the same, over one third said that it was worse and the remaining small minority said that it was neither better or worse. Carers who were still looking after their relatives were much less likely to consider that their lives were better on follow up than those whose relatives were dead or in residential care (seven per cent versus 33 per cent and 47 per cent). Compared to the ex-carers, the carers were much less likely to report better health (six per cent versus 24 per cent), more contact with family and friends or more leisure time.

We showed earlier that the majority of those still caring had to compensate for their relatives' increasing disabilities and, in consequence, they were increasingly pressurised themselves. The comments of these carers, including those of individuals perceiving their lives as the same, suggested that services may be able to do no more than cushion the impact of increasing dependency and weariness. For example, a 70 year old woman caring for her mother, aged 96, said:

> *I'm getting more tired and things are getting on top of me ... I'm much more tense than I was a year ago.*

However, the above daughter now had night sitting services and explained:

> *It's a great help. The nights got so terrible. I don't sleep more but I'm more relaxed and I don't have to get up.*

Small improvements in the carers' lives, which were perhaps all that could be hoped for, were often attributed to the provision of a new service or to increases in the frequency of a service already used. One woman who described her life as, 'more or less the same', but her husband as, 'getting a bit worse', was now using relief care every four instead of every six weeks. She commented:

> *It's better for me - by the time the end of the month comes, I'm ready for a break ... It wouldn't be so bad if he could communicate....*

A son, one of the few still caring who considered that their life was better, said:

> *[Life] is much improved now that they are taking her away for a fortnight every six weeks. I get more help now - and Attendance Allowance.*

We showed in earlier chapters that, once accepted, services were usually used as long as an elderly person remained at home. This observation was confirmed when we compared the services used by the carers at the time of both interviews. This comparison also produced some promising evidence of good practice in the delivery of services. Thus only small numbers of carers had stopped using any of the various services allocated at first interview, and attempts had sometimes been made, for example, to substitute a sitter when day care was no longer appropriate. Moreover, of the 123 carers re-interviewed whose elderly relative remained at home, the proportions allocated day care, sitters or relief care for the first time between interviews were 11 per cent, 10 per cent and 16 per cent respectively. In the case of each of these respite services, about one third of those with the service at both the first and second interviews had enjoyed an increase in the amount of service allocated. In addition, of the 21 carers without respite services on initial interview who remained at home, 10 had begun to use at least one respite service between interviews. The offer of a new service or an increase in the frequency of a service between interviews was related to the level of dependency in the elderly people, suggesting that services responded by increasing their input.

Nonetheless, judging from the carers' and interviewers' comments, there was room for improvements in the responsiveness and quality of long term care management. At follow up, the interviewers explained to the carers that, 'sometimes one person can take on the job of co-ordinating any services or help they think a person in your position might need', and then they asked them: 'Can you think of anyone who does this for you'? Of those still caring, 40 per cent could not identify anyone who co-ordinated their services; interestingly, a further 20 per cent said that they themselves or a member of their family or friends co-ordinated their services. The carers who could identify service co-ordinators were most likely to name community psychiatric nurses and social workers.

The interviewers who were social workers expressed concern about some carers who had looked after their relatives for many years, appeared to have been forgotten by the services and showed signs of great strain. For example, one interviewer was rightly critical of the professionals for failing to review a carer's progress, commenting:

> *There is no key person to plan any respite or monitor any change.*

The importance of monitoring was highlighted by some carers' experiences of the services. The cessation of day hospital care five days a week, for the stated reason that the staff could not handle his severely demented wife, was a great blow to one carer. No other service was offered and this carer said of his life now:

> *It's terrible. It's a 24 hour a day job now that I have retired, because my wife's no longer accepted for day care.*

Another husband, who was in ill-health and close to breaking point, seemed to have nobody monitoring his services. The bath nurse and the transport to day care sometimes did not turn up, the cost of relief care had increased greatly, and the staff at the home sometimes lost his wife's clothes.

By contrast, other carers had benefited from close monitoring of their situation and from reviews of their packages of care. For example, one carer had been allocated an extra day of day care and community nurses now visited him every day to dress and undress his wife. He said:

> *I'm very pleased with the services. Things have changed a bit. She needs more help with physical care and is more confused.*

Nonetheless, despite the carers' heavy workloads and many difficulties, the package of services used by most carers on follow-up was much the same as at the first interviews.

In this context, we found the carers' determination to continue to care impressive. Strikingly, on follow up, 70 per cent of the carers said that they would definitely not accept residential care; and by contrast, only five per cent said that they would definitely accept it. However, thinking about the future, about one fifth of the carers were of the opinion that they were more likely to accept residential care than they had been when first interviewed, mainly because their elderly relatives had deteriorated and they were finding it harder to cope. For example, when asked whether he would accept residential care, one carer said:

Not at the moment. With the help I get, I can cope.

However, there was some change in his feelings about residential care over the year:

I feel more likely to accept it but I wouldn't let her go yet. Last year, we (the family) wouldn't even have thought about it but she's got worse.

This carer, like others, could only foresee accepting residential care when his wife had to be fed and lifted in and out of bed.

In our account of the carers' experiences, we have emphasised that in each outcome group (dead, residential care, at home) the abilities of many elderly people had declined between the first interviews and the last month that they were living at home. We have also emphasised that at the second interviews, the carers of the elderly people who had died and of those who had gone into care were more likely to have said that their own lives had improved and that their health was better than were the carers of elderly people remaining at home. In the next section, we shall show whether changes in the carers' psychological health (GHQ scores) were consistent with their accounts of the stresses of caring and the relief afforded by ceasing to provide daily care.

Changes in the carers' psychological health

In this section, we assess the effects of outcomes for the elderly people on the carers' psychological health. For this purpose, we use the carers' initial and follow up scores on the GHQ to look at changes in their psychological health over the year (Goldberg, 1978). Broadly, a decrease in GHQ score at the second interview suggests improved psychological health; conversely, an increase in GHQ score suggests a deterioration in psychological health.

We began the analysis by establishing whether the initial and follow up GHQ scores of each carer were above or below the now familiar threshold of 5/6 (the higher the score above the threshold, the higher the probability that an individual is experiencing symptoms associated with depression, anxiety and hypochondriacal self-concern).

On the basis of both the carers' scores, we divided them into four groups, as shown in Table 8.7. The first group was made up of those whose initial and follow up GHQ scores were both less than six, suggesting the absence of psychological disturbance at both interviews. The second group was made up of those who had initial GHQ scores of less than six but follow up scores of six and over, suggesting a deterioration in their psychological health over the year. The third group had initial GHQ scores of six and over but follow up GHQ scores of less than six, suggesting an improvement in their mental health. The final group had both initial and follow up GHQ scores of six and over; at both interviews, therefore, the probability of psychological disturbance was high.

Table 8.7 The Change in 'Caseness' of the Carers' GHQ Scores between First and Follow Up Interview by Outcomes for the Elderly People

	Outcomes for the Elderly People				Significance
	At Home %	In Care %	Dead %	Overall %	
Change in GHQ Scores					
Stay < 6	53	41	42	47	
Low to high	19	5	9	14	chi-sqr 18
High to low	10	26	23	17	$p = 0.006$
Stay > 6	18	28	26	22	
Total	*123*	*39*	*81*	*243*	

The first column of Table 8.7 shows what had happened to the mental health of the carers who were still looking after an elderly person. First, we can see that 53 per cent of these carers were free from psychological symptoms at both interviews. The next figure in the column is more worrying: the GHQ scores of 19 per cent of those still caring had moved from below to above the threshold of 5/6, suggesting that the probability of psychological disturbance had moved from low to high over the year. The next figure in the column did not surprise us: only 10 per cent of those still caring showed signs of improved mental health, a proportion which was smaller than those who showed signs of a deterioration in mental health. The last figure in the column, however, was a cause for concern: almost one fifth of those still caring had symptoms of psychological disturbance at the first interview which had persisted over the year.

These findings alone raise some important issues. First, on the evidence of both the initial and follow up interviews, the psychological health of those looking after a person with dementia in our sample seemed, on average, worse than that of random samples of the ordinary population. Second, we knew that only some of those who were likely to have a psychiatric illness at follow up were receiving professional help. Third, given the association we had established between the carers' GHQ scores and the problems they faced in caring, and, in addition, the association between the carers' initial GHQ scores and the outcomes for the elderly people, we thought that both the carers with high GHQ scores at second interview and the persons for whom they cared might be vulnerable groups.

The next two columns on Table 8.7 also contain some interesting findings, not least because of the marked similarities between the two of them. First, it can be seen that 41 per cent of the carers of an elderly person who had entered residential care and, 42 per cent of the carers of an elderly person who had died had few symptoms of psychological disturbance at both the first interview and one year later. Second, it can be seen that only a very small minority in each of these outcome groups showed signs of a deterioration in their psychological health, especially when we looked at the comparable proportions among those who were still caring. Third, 27 per cent of those who had ceased to provide daily care showed signs of improved mental health (compared with only 10 per cent of those still caring). Finally, an important finding was that over one quarter of those who were caring at the first interview but not at the second interview had psychological symptoms which had persisted over the year.

Once again, these findings suggested the importance of paying attention to the carers' mental health not only whilst they were caring but also in the months after they had ceased to provide care: at the very least, the carers should surely be informed of the professional help available if they required it. Furthermore, the finding that about one third of the carers who had ceased to provide care showed signs of psychological disturbance at follow up suggested that the relinquishment of the caregiving role was not always beneficial to a carer's mental health, at least in the short term. This disquieting result was very similar to that of a comparable study of French caregivers which suggested that a year after admission to care, unhappiness was expressed by one third of the carers, principally due to the role loss, financial and family problems, and poor contact with residential care staff (Ritchie and Ledésert, 1992). On the evidence of both the carers' comments and their GHQ scores, residential care was the only service which could relieve the distress which some carers experienced; on the same evidence, there was a need to develop alternative approaches to the alleviation of psychological distress in others.

In a second analysis, we compared the magnitude and direction of the change, on average, in the psychological health of the carers across the outcome groups, adjusting for the association of difference in GHQ score with initial GHQ score.

The first column of Table 8.8 shows that the mean initial GHQ score of the carers of elderly people who subsequently remained at home was lower than the comparable score for each of the other two outcome groups. The last column of Table 8.8 shows a mean decrease in the GHQ scores of the carers of elderly people who entered residential care or died subsequently, but not in the score of the carers of elderly people who remained at home. In other words, the carers who had ceased to provide daily care showed, on average, signs of improved psychological health. In contrast, those who were still looking after an elderly person showed, on average, no such signs of improvement.

Table 8.8 The Carers' Initial and Follow Up GHQ Scores by Outcomes for the Elderly People

| | Carers' GHQ scores | | | |
	Initial mean	Follow up mean	Difference mean	*N* at follow up
At follow up elderly people				
At home	4.19	5.19	1.00	*123*
In care	8.44	5.54	-2.90[4]	*39*
Dead	7.04	5.65	-1.38	*81*
Total	**15.82**	**5.40**	**-0.42**	**243**
(± 95% CL)	(±0.77)	(±0.82)	(±0.75)	
F value	10.3	0.14	2.91	
p value	0.0001	0.87	0.056	
Least significant difference test:				
At home vs In care	*	ns	*	
At home vs Dead	*	ns	*	
In care vs Dead	ns	ns	ns	

* denotes pairs of groups significantly different at the $p = 0.05$ level.

Notes

1. 44 cases were missing at follow up. These 44 have been excluded from the initial GHQ score.

2. Statistical tests of the mean *change* in GHQ score are based on analyses of co-variance with the initial GHQ score as the co-variate.

3. The GHQ difference is calculated as the follow up GHQ minus the initial GHQ score. A negative difference in GHQ scores indicates an improvement in mental health.

4. This improvement in GHQ score is even greater for those carers who stated at first interview that they would accept residential care (see Table 8.9).

Once we had established the positive effects, on average, of ceasing to provide care on the carers' psychological health, we sought to identify the carers who appeared to benefit most from residential care services. We were constrained by the small number of carers in this group but compared them in terms of the characteristics of the carers and the elderly people, and in terms of their use of services at the first interview.

Of the many dimensions we examined, the sharpest contrast in the effect of residential care was found between those who would have accepted residential care and those who would not have accepted it a year earlier.

Table 8.9 The Change in the Carers' GHQ Scores by their Attitude to Residential Care at First Interview and Outcomes for the Elderly People

| | Mean Change in GHQ Score for Carers with Elderly People: | | | |
	At Home	In Care	Dead	Overall
Carer would accept residential care				
Yes	1.00	-6.12	-4.58	-4.32
N	7	17	26	50
No	1.03	-0.15	0.13	0.64
N	113	20	54	187
Overall	1.02	-2.89	-1.40	0.41
N	120	37	80	237
t value	-	3.52	3.48	5.47
p value		0.002	0.001	0.000

As we show in the second column of Table 8.9 placement of an elderly person in residential care brought, on average, benefit to the psychological health of those who would have accepted residential care, but no such benefit to those who would not have accepted it, at least in the months immediately following admission.

Once again, our results showed that the characteristics of the carers, especially their attitude to permanent care and their mental health at the first interviews were crucial. Whatever, the number and type of respite services used, there was a drop, on average, in the carers' GHQ scores if they had ceased to provide care a year later; while the size of the drop did not vary with service use at first interview, it varied with the carers' attitude towards residential care.

Among the carers of elderly people who remained at home, we have looked also in detail at the relationship between their characteristics and their use of services at first interview and changes in the carers' mental health over the subsequent year. We have been unable to identify a group of carers who showed a mean decrease in their GHQ scores, suggesting better psychological health a year later. Irrespective of the characteristics and services examined, their GHQ scores remained, on average, stable over the year and the direction of the change, if any, was always an increase, rather than a decrease, in their GHQ scores.

This finding is not as disappointing as it may appear on the surface. The carers had completed another year of caregiving, one fifth of them had new psychological symptoms, the abilities of many of the elderly people had deteriorated, and the services received over the year had not increased substantially. It may be unreasonable, therefore, to expect a detectable effect of services of the psychological health of these carers. However, we shall continue to explore this issue taking account of changes in the elderly people and service use over the year and report our results in later publications.

Our finding that residential care is the service which brings, on average, improvements to the carers' mental health are among the most important of the study. They are consistent with the small but growing number of studies which have reached the same conclusion, despite differences in their methods and their study populations (Gilleard, 1987; Wells and Jorm, 1987; Levin *et al.*, 1989; Wells *et al.*, 1990). Without exception, these researchers comment on the modest respite provided by ordinary services, compared with that provided by residential care and they emphasise the carers' positive evaluation of these modest services. They call for increased efforts to provide the carers with a variety of types of help and to close the gap between the intensive break afforded by residential care and that afforded by community services.

Conclusions

We have tackled many questions in this chapter and we shall simply summarise here the key findings which have the greatest implications for the carers and the services.

First, seven in ten of the elderly people who were alive at follow up were still cared for at home. This finding seems particularly impressive in the light of the high level of dependency and behavioural difficulty in this sample of elderly people.

Second, the abilities of most elderly people continued to decline, and, as a result, their carers faced increased pressure in the last month of caring.

Third, attributes of the carer, especially their attitude to residential care and their mental health were among the main predictors of whether an elderly person remained at home or entered residential care.

Fourth, the carers of elderly people who had entered residential care showed, on average, signs of improved mental health at follow up, especially if they had wanted residential care at the first interviews.

Finally, the carers continued to use respite services and to value them. Indeed, in the face of increasing deterioration in the elderly people, many carers said that they could not have coped without services. However, respite services were neither very intensive nor very flexible . For example, most carers with sitting services were given a break of about three hours once a week and elderly people with day care attended on average twice a week.

Given the heavy reliance of these elderly people on their carers for survival at home, it may be unrealistic to expect that standard services could have a detectable impact on the carers' psychological health or prevent entirely the entry of elderly people with moderate or severe dementia into residential care in the last months of their lives.

On our evidence, respite services continue to be used to serve three purposes: first, they are used to ration and postpone the use of permanent care which some carers, albeit a minority, would have preferred; second, they are used to prepare both the carer and the elderly person gradually for permanent care; and third, they are used to support carers who want to continue to provide care. These services cannot substitute for permanent care. Nevertheless, the carers' positive views of the services must be taken very seriously. It may be realistic, therefore, to measure the usefulness of respite by assessing the extent to which they alleviate the precise problems that these carers face.

Finally, the policy of community care for elderly people with moderate or severe dementia can be difficult to achieve without imposing substantial burdens on many carers. The carers who no longer had to provide care showed signs of improved mental health, and those who continued to provide care did not. Residential care, therefore, is an option which needs to be available to these carers. But a key question is whether more intensive community services could substantially alleviate the burden faced by those who want or have to continue to look after elderly people with moderate or severe dementia at home?

9   Conclusions

Introduction

This study took place at a time when *Caring for People* (1989) and the *National Health Service and Community Care Act 1990* signalled major changes in the arrangements for community care. The statement in *Caring for People* that:

> *A key responsibility of statutory service providers should be to do all they can to assist and support carers*
>
> (Secretaries of State, 1989, p.9)

was an explicit recognition of the contribution of families, friends and neighbours in enabling people to continue to live in the community. Our study has sought to describe the day to day experiences of one group, those who lived with a confused elderly person for whom they cared, and to document the strengths and weaknesses of services set up to support and assist them.

Respite provides one of the few examples of a service aimed directly at carers (Audit Commission, 1992). Definitions of what this entails vary, but they generally reflect an intention to provide time off, or a break, from caring responsibilities. In this study we looked at home based schemes whereby a sitter or carers' support worker took over from or assisted the carer. We also considered respite services provided outside the home in day centres or day hospitals. Finally, we examined longer breaks away from home, where the person cared for spent time in relief care in hospitals, residential or nursing homes, or in home like settings provided by family based respite care schemes. This task took us to three different areas of England and we spanned the full range of provision across health and social services, voluntary organisations, privately and informally arranged sources.

In writing these conclusions, we have several purposes. Earlier chapters in this book have provided very specific details about respite services individually and in combination. In this one, we shall try to outline our findings in general but our themes will be broader in their scope. We intend to address the question of the relevance of respite services and the extent to which they provide carers with practical help. In highlighting areas in which improvements might be made, we shall be especially mindful of what we believe will be the relevant key areas for future community care services.

These issues are of vital importance for all those concerned with community care. From the perspective of those involved in policy development and in purchasing services, clear information is needed on the numbers of people likely to be using respite, the extent of their service use, and the impact that this is likely to have on community and residential services as a whole in the future. Those who are providing respite care might wish to make use of our material on the preferences of carers and users, the types of services they find helpful and those that are unhelpful. We hope that those who are caring themselves may find what we have written of some pertinence. It is also important to place our study in the context of existing research on carers and services.

Any work which hopes to reach across audiences carries the risk of falling between two stools. We hope that, as we draw together the main findings of the study and assess their implications, one single theme will emerge, concerned with helping to improve the quality of respite services for carers and those for whom they care.

The context for future service provision

Decisions about expenditure on community care have to be made in the light of statutory requirements, such as those laid out in the *Children Act 1989* and the *NHS and Community Care Act 1990*, funding constraints, and many other competing priorities. Our sample consisted of carers, nearly all of whom were looking after a person with a diagnosis of Alzheimer's disease or a related disorder, yet resources must be shared out across many different people. Why, then, should we lay such importance upon the needs of one group?

Estimating how many people are affected by dementia

Community surveys in Great Britain have consistently estimated that around five per cent of the population over the age of 65 have moderate or severe dementia. This figure may increase to about seven per cent when people in residential care are included. Over the next twenty years, the number of elderly people in Great Britain with moderate or severe dementia is projected to increase by 30,000 to 684,000. If we include those with mild dementia, by 2001, the total may have risen to around three quarters of a million (ADS, 1993).

What is the importance of these figures in the context of the rise in the proportions of people aged 75 and over in the population as a whole?

This stems from the prevalence rate of dementia which doubles with each additional 5.1 years of age (Jorm and Korten, 1988). While there is a debate over the extent to which this exponential increase can be seen beyond the age of 85, the key point to remember is that almost 20 per cent of people in the 80 to 84 age group might be expected to show symptoms consistent with a diagnosis of dementia.

Admittedly, the estimates outlined above are based solely on population figures and age specific prevalence rates. Indeed, an increase of five per cent in the numbers of elderly people with moderate or severe dementia in the next ten years is much smaller than the comparable increases in the 1970's and the 1980's. There are also fundamental problems in calculating dementia free life expectancy and survival rates for people with dementia, although these have clear implications for service provision (Ritchie, 1992). In addition, despite important advances in medical research, we cannot predict whether the causes of Alzheimer's disease and related disorders will become more fully understood or whether specific drug treatments will be shown to have a lasting effectiveness. These factors notwithstanding, it seems likely that there will be a growing number of elderly people with dementia who will continue to require care in the immediate future. This has clear implications for the allocation of resources.

Use of services

How does the picture outlined above fit into the way community care services are provided? Recent research has confirmed that elderly people with dementia are particularly likely to use domiciliary and respite services. In the case of those with moderate and severe dementia, service use is likely to be multiple (O'Connor *et al.*, 1989; Livingston *et al.*, 1990). More specifically, our previous research (Levin *et al.*, 1989) showed that the package of day and relief care was generally used by the carers of elderly people with moderate or severe dementia who required a great deal of help and manifested many behavioural difficulties.

In the long term, the presence of a dementing illness greatly increases the likelihood that an elderly person will enter continuing residential care (Opit and Pahl, 1993). Indeed, it is estimated that more than half of the elderly people in residential care have diagnoses of Alzheimer's disease or a related disorder (Sinclair *et al.*, 1990).

The impact on families and carers

In conjunction with the arguments surrounding incidence, prevalence and service use, there is a third and especially important reason why we believe that future community care provision must acknowledge the importance of services for the type of carers and elderly people in our study. This is the impact that conditions such as Alzheimer's disease or related disorders can have upon families. By virtue of the progressive loss of the ability to think, remember and reason, the people affected find increasing difficulties in looking after themselves and, in consequence, become very reliant upon the help of others. Yet, research has indicated that the majority of these people live in the community and that most would prefer to remain in their own homes. Similarly, their carers also wish to continue to look after them as long as possible.

Set against these preferences, we should also bear in mind that caring for a person with dementia has been shown to be a greater source of stress than caring for a person without dementia. The stresses associated with caring can have a long term impact because, as reviews of the literature have shown, over the period of a year, it is the mental health of those carers whose relatives die or enter residential care which improves, rather than that of those who continue to care (Sinclair *et al.*, 1990).

Who carries the heaviest responsibilities for caring?

There is no doubt that increasing recognition has been given to carers' needs over the last few years. As our knowledge base has increased, researchers have questioned how best we may take it forward. This has resulted in a keen debate over how the numbers and types of carers can be classified and categorised. As part of her contribution to this discourse, Parker has suggested that individuals providing *personal or physical* assistance are likely to be heavily involved in that:

1. *They provide longer hours of help*

2. *They are more likely to be helping with no assistance from other people*

3. *They are looking after someone who lives in the same household*

4. *They carry out more helping activities in total*

5. *The person they are supporting is more likely to have some form of mental impairment.*

(Parker, 1992, p.14)

As we turn to our summary of the characteristics of the sample, the extent of the carers' responsibilities will become clear.

The characteristics of the elderly people in the sample

In this study, we used the term 'confused elderly people' as shorthand to take account of the fact that, in order to include the full range of respite services, not everyone in the sample would have been referred to a psychogeriatrician or geriatrician and been given a recognised diagnosis of Alzheimer's disease or a related disorder. Nevertheless, on the basis of the measures which we used, around 80 per cent of the 287 elderly people in the sample showed evidence of moderate or severe dementia.

On a day to day basis their carers were dealing with a wide range of problems in the elderly people, such as incontinence, acting unsafely (for instance, attempting to place electric kettles on cookers), disturbed nights, an inability to express themselves clearly in conversation, trying behaviours such as restlessness, repetition and aggression and apathy.

Around sixty per cent of the elderly people also suffered from other health problems. The most frequent conditions suffered by the elderly people and reported by their carers were arthritis and cerebrovascular accidents. This was to be expected, given the type of sample selected.

Overall, at the time that the first interviews took place, half the elderly people came into the most dependent category of the Behaviour Rating Scale (BRS) (Pattie and Gilleard, 1979) and required help with almost every aspect of their personal care. In keeping with this picture, half of the carers were unwilling or unable to leave the person for whom they cared for alone in the house. We should also remember that the overwhelming likelihood was that these problems would worsen rather than improve, with a consequent effect not only upon the elderly people themselves, but also upon those who cared for them.

The characteristics of the carers in the sample

Caring for people with the sorts of problems outlined above would require a considerable degree of commitment from anyone. It is rendered all the more impressive when we consider that over 60 per cent of the carers were aged 65 and over and that many had health problems of their own. The vast majority were married to, or an adult child of, the people for whom they cared. The amount of help that they gave usually far outstripped that given by others. Indeed, when the carers were asked to estimate their amount of time off per week, the average total amounted to 16 hours. Given the length and intensity of their responsibilities, it was not surprising that 90 per cent of the carers felt themselves to be restricted in some way because of caring.

At first interview, a huge majority of carers wanted to continue looking after their relatives at home. However, there was evidence that the difficulties and stresses of caring were taking their toll. Forty per cent of the carers scored between six and 28 on the 28 item version of General Health Questionnaire (GHQ). This suggested that these carers were likely to be experiencing symptoms associated with conditions such as anxiety, depression and hypochondriacal self concern (Goldberg and Williams, 1988). Gender played an important part, with women scoring more highly than men, even when we controlled for age and health status. Using our second measure, the SELFCARE (D), 25 per cent of the carers had scores indicative of a depressive illness (Bird *et al.*, 1987).

So far, we have argued that the elderly people in our sample had needs which pose great challenges to community care services overall. We have also suggested that their carers' contribution was very great. What, then, were the sorts of respite service which they might expect to receive?

Types and mixes of respite services

A mix of respite services is required to take account of the unique and changing needs of carers and those for whom they care. The challenge is to ensure a degree of choice for those people wishing to use respite while ensuring that, at the same time, such services are targeted upon those with the greatest needs. To what extent was this being achieved?

As we would have expected from a sample largely consisting of people in the later stages of Alzheimer's disease or a related disorder, 85 per cent of the elderly people and their carers used at least one respite service. The elderly people without respite services generally consisted of those who had been referred to services relatively recently and showed fewer signs of cognitive impairment and of needing help with their personal care and other activities of living.

Further support for this picture came from the fact that the elderly people with one service were generally less dependent than those using two. Across the whole of the sample, the most frequent package was that of day and relief care, used by just under 40 per cent of those with any respite services.

Next, the inclusion of relief care in a package with its potential for a longer break for the carer, was associated with much higher levels of cognitive impairment and dependency on the part of the elderly person. Thus, elderly people using day care or sitting singly or in combination were less dependent than those with any sort of relief care.

Taking all this together, there were clear signs that, at the time of the study, some targeting of respite services in accordance with the needs of the elderly people was already taking place. This raises important questions about the principles upon which services will be targeted. In the context of our sample, elderly people with relatively low levels of service inputs were, on average, less dependent and cognitively impaired. In other samples, such as those including all the frail elderly, their care requirements might be regarded as considerable. Furthermore, targeting upon the basis of dependency in the person cared for was all very well when the service offered did not conflict with the preferences of carer and elderly person. Problems occurred when there was a divergence. For instance, not every carer or elderly person who rejected day care was offered a sitter as an alternative. Similarly, it was irrelevant if the elderly person met the criteria for being offered relief care if he or she and the carer did not wish to be separated.

Previous research and the experiences of the professionals with whom we spoke have suggested that services often intervene in response to strain. While in some senses our finding that respite services were targeted upon carers with high GHQ scores was positive, in others, it could be argued that what opportunity does this create for them to operate preventatively by intervening *before* there has been a build up of strain and difficulty for the carer?

The successful, albeit qualified, targeting of respite services was not matched by the degree of choice open to carers and those for whom they cared. In general, respite services in each of the three study areas were delivered in standard amounts at standard intervals. The uniformity of the packages suggested that usually the carers had to fit into the services available and that there was limited scope for providing flexibility and choice within existing resources.

Our analyses of the types, mixes, availability and extent of respite services led us to conclude that lack of choice in their type and timing meant that they were only a partial solution to the restrictions and other difficulties due to caring. There was little evidence that resources could be switched from those services which were currently provided in order to develop others. However, as we have already suggested, projections of service use and (as we hope to show below) the carers' appreciation both make it seem likely that the demand for such services will continue, and may increase.

Were respite services appreciated?

Most carers using sitting or day care were of the opinion that the elderly people derived some direct benefit from the sitter's visits and from attendance at day care. Opinions were more divided about the effects of relief care on the elderly people, with a much higher proportion of carers reporting that the service did not bring any benefits to the person cared for but recognising that they themselves would be unable to continue without this source of time off from caring.

For nearly all the carers, respite services were useful, often indispensable. For example, day care gave the carers a break for about six hours usually twice a week. This enabled them to undertake essential tasks such as cleaning and shopping, gave them some choice about going out, and some time to relax and pursue their own interests.

Sitters and care attendants afforded the carers a shorter break. Typically, they were provided once a week for about three and a half hours during the morning or afternoon. The carers almost always went out using the time to go shopping, to the bank, to visit the hairdressers, and to see relatives and friends.

Relief care in hospitals, homes or family based respite care gave a more complete break than that provided by day care or sitting. Most carers using this service were on packages ranging in frequency from six to 12 week intervals between breaks, and by far the commonest length of break was a fortnight. Relief care gave them the opportunity to rest and recuperate, to have free evenings and weekends, to have a holiday, to devote more time to other relatives and friends, and to maintain their homes.

The relevance and value of respite services was emphasised further by the finding that once the carers had been allocated these services, the great majority made continuing use of them. When they were first interviewed, substantial minorities of carers had been using respite services for more than two years. On follow up, the majority of those who were still carers had continued with the services received at first interview. In some cases, these services were more frequent and, in others, additional forms of respite had been included. Of those whose elderly relatives had died or had entered residential care, they had generally continued to use respite services right up until their last month of caring.

Towards more responsive respite services

One of the underpinning purposes behind the provision of respite services is the intention to alleviate sources of stress for carers. We have said that they were nearly always targeted in line with the dependency of the elderly people, yet in a sample such as ours, much is evidently dependent upon the carer's abilities and wish to continue caring. Therefore, close attention to the carer's needs is a prerequisite to successful community care, a point which is clearly emphasised in the practice guidance (SSI/SWSG, 1991b).

Our analyses of the carers' GHQ scores and the amount of help which they received from their family and friends highlighted some points which we believe should be given attention when carers and elderly people are being assessed for their suitability for respite services.

Help from family and friends

Across all carers, not just those in our sample, there is no doubt that some will share their caring responsibilities with other members of their family, friends and neighbours. Nonetheless, even in these instances, there are likely to be limits to the type and amount of help they might expect to receive. Where help with the personal care of another person is required, it is usually family members (and in particular those living in the same household), who are the providers (Arber and Ginn, 1991; Wenger, 1992).

Did the carers in our sample have others whom they could ask to take over the care of the elderly person? Seventy per cent lived with the elderly person alone and so it was unlikely that there was another person available on the spot to share the carer's role. What about family and friends living nearby? Not everyone had other sources of help available. For instance, 25 per cent of the elderly people had no living children. Although most of the carers had relatives and friends who visited, telephoned and, in some instances, gave practical help, less than half had someone who had taken over from them for a few hours during the day. A longer break was even more unusual; over the year prior to the first interview, only 11 per cent of the carers could remember another person in their family or a friend who had looked after the elderly person for a period of 24 hours or longer.

The carer's health

Carers who rated their health as poor and those who reported a longstanding illness or disability were likely to have higher GHQ scores. Their comments indicated that they were less inclined to want to go out and visit friends or pursue hobbies for the duration of respite services. Respite services in the form of care attendants might be most helpful for these carers. Their health status is likely to make it more difficult for them to carry out intensive personal care tasks and so, not only would they have someone with whom to share their caring responsibilities, but they would also be given a source of social contact and support.

Leisure and time off from caring

Lack of leisure time, feelings of loneliness and not seeing family and friends often enough were all associated with high GHQ scores. A related problem is the difficulty the carers found fitting in responsibilities additional to those of the role of carer, such as those to other family members or as an employee. Carers feeling socially isolated and restricted and those with competing responsibilities might especially benefit from respite services which take over the care of the elderly person, enabling the carer to visit friends, pursue hobbies, and so on.

Characteristics of the person cared for

Factors such as disturbed sleep patterns at night, incontinence, trying behaviours and overall dependency were associated with higher GHQ scores. There is scope here for advising carers on developing specific strategies to deal with these problems. However, of equal importance is an acknowledgement that caring can become an unremitting task in these circumstances. It is important that the types and amounts of respite offered are commensurate with the degree of the carer's responsibilities. One day a week at day care may have been all that was required when the person cared for had only recently been diagnosed as having Alzheimer's disease or a related disorder; as his or her condition worsened, it was likely to be insufficient.

We found that carers who stated in the interview that they wanted additional respite services were likely to have high GHQ scores yet it has been shown repeatedly that carers are reluctant to ask outright for more help. We believe that this suggests that those arranging services must be as alert as possible to picking up signals that the carer feels in need of more assistance, even though he or she may not have asked for this directly.

Our review of carers' sources of help, their opportunities for caring, and the degree of help and supervision they were giving, led us to reach the very firm conclusion that many were almost entirely reliant upon services for time off from caring. Plans for future provision of community care services need to take account of the primacy of existing sitting, day and relief care services in giving carers the chance of a regular break.

Other suggestions for improvement

Day care

Day care was the main service providing a regular break to the carers. For carers coping with moderate or severe dementia, we found that the great majority used it in combination with relief care. In Chapter Five, we presented evidence in support of some detailed suggestions on the scope for improvements in the service at the point of its arrangement, in the quality of the programme, and in its availability and flexibility.

Our suggestions for priorities in the development of day care services centre around the way it is provided, the amount available, and its quality. It is essential that a coherent pattern of day care services is developed which takes account of the overlapping contribution of health and social care agencies, and explores the option of providing locality based, rather than sector based, day care. This should minimise the need for elderly people to attend more than one venue in order to get additional amounts of day care.

Most day care was provided on weekdays between 9.00 a.m. and 5.00 p.m. Increasing the hours available and ensuring that it is available at weekends would extend carers' options for leisure or employment prospects. It would also mean carers could choose between extended day care or relief care.

Our recommendations for improvements to the quality of day care highlight the need to improve transport services and to ensure that there is a wide range of activities allowing for individualised programmes. There is also scope for improving contact between day care staff and carers, promoting a sense of partnership and continuity.

Sitting and carers' support schemes

Unlike day and relief care, these services have yet to become part of mainstream provision. In our study, only a minority had access to sitting services. Furthermore, mainstream home care services were not providing a substitute. Evidence of under provision came from carers with the service who would have liked a more frequent and flexible service, and from carers without the service who would have wished to have a sitter or carers' support worker.

We have identified improvements which might be made to sitting services in Chapter Six. Here, our key recommendation is that planners accord top priority to the development of home based respite services. In addition to those sitting services provided by voluntary organisations, purchasing the service from independent consortia or agencies, or extending home care services, are all options which might be followed. This will increase choice for carers, particularly those caring for people who are unwilling or unsuitable to attend day care.

Relief care

For most carers, relief care was nearly always their sole source of a break longer than 24 hours. Targeted as it was upon the most severely dependent and behaviourally disturbed elderly people in the sample, for some carers it was an intermediate service prior to the elderly person's admission to residential care. For others, the service showed potential for enabling those carers who wanted to continue to care, despite the high levels of help required by the person cared for, to continue to do so.

Given the reluctance of some carers to use relief care and the ambivalence with which it was viewed even by those using the service, we believe that it is important that attention is paid to achieving greater clarity surrounding the purpose of relief care. When it is to be included in a package of services, the carer, if possible the person cared for, and those arranging the service need to discuss fully whether it is to be part of a long term strategy to enable the elderly person to remain at home or whether permanent residential care is likely in the short to medium term. Such decisions will influence the venue, form, timing and frequency of breaks arranged.

It is also vital to develop more flexible relief care services which offer a break of the length and frequency that the carer chooses. Although residential relief care is likely to continue to be necessary, developing family based schemes would also help, especially as some carers said that they would prefer this to care in an institution.

Lastly, attention should be given to improving and monitoring the quality of relief care so that the elderly people have as positive an experience as possible. The Social Services Inspectorate have suggested that this is an important consideration when laying down standards for this type of break (SSI, 1993).

Establishing outcomes

A follow up interview with the carers took place approximately one year after the first interview. We were able to establish outcomes for all of the 287 elderly people and for 280 of the carers. Our reinterview rate was just under 85 per cent (243 cases) because in addition to those carers whom we were unable to trace, some preferred not to be reinterviewed and others had, sadly, died or become too ill themselves to participate.

Thirty five per cent of the elderly people died in the period between first and follow up interviews. We were not surprised by this, given the targeting of respite services upon those who were most dependent. What was remarkable was that, of the elderly people who were still alive, 72 per cent remained at home. Including those who had died, this might be expressed as just under half of the sample.

So those remaining elderly people who had entered some form of residential care were indeed in the minority (*n*=53). Forty three per cent of this small group were in residential or nursing homes in the independent sector. Around a quarter were in NHS wards or specialist NHS units for people with mental health problems in old age. Those elderly people who had entered NHS hospitals or nursing homes were more severely cognitively impaired and dependent than those who had entered local authority homes or residential and nursing homes in the independent sector. The role of the NHS in providing continuing care for people with terminal illnesses, such as the advanced stages of Alzheimer's disease has, of course, been set out in paragraphs 4.19 to 4.23 of *Caring for People* (1989).

Factors associated with different outcomes

What then were the factors which predicted outcomes? Certainly, there was a relationship with the degree of cognitive impairment. Those who were markedly or severely impaired were less likely to have remained at home. This was also noted in a study of patients referred to a psychogeriatric unit (Reddy and Pitt, 1993).

Did the respite services received have any effect? We were not surprised that there was no difference in outcomes by study area. Although we have stressed the differences that existed, they were not so great as to have substantially altered the levels of provision any of the carers might have expected to receive.

The outcome for elderly people using different packages of respite did vary. Elderly people using day care and/or sitting services, but not relief care, were more likely to remain at home than those who used these services in conjunction with relief care. This confirms that it is indeed useful to divide the users of day care and sitting services into two groups on the basis of whether they use residential respite or not. Certainly, elderly people with relief care were more dependent. More importantly, we would argue that among the carers with relief care, their higher GHQ scores and greater willingness to consider residential care suggested that they were reaching the limits of their capacity to care.

Our study provided fresh evidence that respite services are offered for very different reasons. After they had accepted day or relief care, some carers had continued to look after the person for whom they cared for a much longer period than others. Others appeared only to have been offered these services when they were finding their caring responsibilities more difficult.

It was the attributes of the *carers* which had the major influence upon whether the person cared for was at home or in residential care on follow up. This serves to emphasise just why it is so essential to set such store upon assessing their needs when arranging respite and other community services.

We identified two major differences between the carers of elderly people who remained at home and the carers of those who had gone into residential care or had died. Those who had higher GHQ and SELFCARE (D) scores at first interview were more likely to have been caring for elderly people who had been placed in residential care or had died over the year preceding the follow up interview. On these measures, these carers were more likely to have been experiencing symptoms associated with depression and anxiety.

Of even greater magnitude was the association between the carers' attitude to residential care at first interview and outcomes for the elderly people. Eighty six per cent of those elderly people whose carer would have definitely or probably accepted it at first interview had died or entered permanent residential care by the time of the follow up interviews. The guidance given in *Community Care in the Next Decade and Beyond* states that:

> *The preferences of carers should be taken into account and their willingness to continue caring should not be assumed.*
>
> *(DH, 1990, p.28)*

We would suggest that it is vital that care managers ensure that they have considered carers' attitudes towards residential care when first arranging community care services.

Furthermore, the death or a breakdown in the health of the carer almost always precipitated the elderly person's placement in residential care. Thus, the survival at home of the elderly people hinged almost entirely upon the carer; other relatives were rarely available or willing to substitute in the long term, and services could not provide the intensity of cover required for the elderly people to live safely and comfortably at home.

If so much was dependent upon the carers in the sample and yet previous research suggested that ceasing to care would have a beneficial effect upon their mental health, did we have any indication where respite services might have had an effect? Using the GHQ, we compared changes in the scores of the carers whose relatives were in residential care with those who continued to care. Overall, the mental health of carers improved, on average, if the elderly person were admitted to residential care. The mental health of those who continued to provide care, often in the face of deterioration in the elderly people and little (if any) increase in the services received, showed no such change.

We would argue that this seems to support the viewpoint that it is important not to set too much store on the potential of very limited amounts of service provision. There is no doubt that for some carers, residential care created new or compounded old stresses. Some carers continued to play an active part in the care of the elderly person in the residential care setting. Nevertheless, for the purpose of this argument, let us see residential care as the equivalent of 168 hours of respite a week. Compare this with 12 hours day care and four hours sitting each week, and a fortnight's relief care every six weeks and we can see that the most intensive package of respite services which carers in the sample were likely to be offered could not approach this figure. Thus, once a carer's GHQ score was above the threshold of six, it was unlikely that he or she would be offered respite services at an intensity and in amounts which would be likely to have an effect comparable with that of ceasing to care.

The implications for community care services in the future

Although the thrust of our study was upon respite services, and its time span from 1988 until 1991 meant that it was completed before the final implementation of community care arrangements in April 1993, we feel that the information we collected from the carers about the processes by which respite services were arranged might offer some useful insights in anticipation of future research into community care.

Planning future provision

Each of the services in the three study areas aimed to support the carers of elderly people with dementia, but there was marked variation in the overall mix and level of provision. There was scope for extending provision and re-thinking the relative contributions of local authority, health, voluntary and independent sector provision. The patchwork of services appeared to have developed over time in an unco-ordinated manner, with consequences for its current responsiveness to local needs.

Many of those involved in community care provision may have already drawn up a joint inventory of current provision of respite services and identified priority areas for development as part of their community care plans. We recommend that those who have not, should do this as part of their strategy for respite services.

Assessing and arranging respite services

Many practitioners and care agencies were involved in providing the complex mixes of services. The professionals involved in assessing and reassessing the need for services included general practitioners, psychogeriatricians, social workers, nurses, home care organisers, and sitting and day care co-ordinators. Our conclusion is that elderly people with dementia and their carers will be the groups posing the greatest challenges to community care services, given that assessments at the most complex levels will be required, and that their packages of care will almost inevitably span across health and social care.

Styles of care management and collaborative working

Services in the three study areas provided examples of different approaches to arranging care, each of which had its own strengths. In each area, the contribution made by health care professionals, including psychogeriatricians, geriatricians, and community psychiatric nurses, was substantial. The need for close involvement between health and social care agencies will continue to be necessary. Our findings suggested that the task of long term care management was complex and that there was scope for improvement in co-operation between professionals and in direct work with elderly people and their carers.

Improving practices in arranging care

Both social workers and community psychiatric nurses were performing the tasks broadly equivalent to those of care managers but half the carers could not recall a time when a professional had told them about the full range of services available, and more than half of the carers could not identify a professional who was co-ordinating their services. They might also have benefited from greater and more formal involvement in reviews of care packages.

We have three priorities for improving policy and practice in arranging care. First, elderly people, their carers and the professionals working with them need to have up to date information about services. Second, collaborative care management systems should exist which take account of the complex needs of elderly people with dementia and their carers, and of the range of professionals and agencies required to meet them. Finally, standards of good practice in care management should be set and arrangements made for monitoring progress towards their achievement. These should cover the provision of clear information and explanations to carers including the name of their care manager, how to contact him or her, how the process of assessment and review works, how they (the carers) will be involved, the range of service options available and how to follow the complaints procedure. All these practices are consistent with the advice given in the policy guidance documents (DH, 1990; SSI/SSWG, 1991a; 1991b).

The need for long term care management

Irrespective of whether the elderly people in the sample would ultimately enter residential care, by far the longest proportion of time since the carers had noticed symptoms consistent with a diagnosis of Alzheimer's disease or a related disorder would have been spent in living in the community. We believe that this reinforces the need for care managers to take a long term view when arranging community care services and to ensure that those packages arranged are regularly reviewed.

Access to respite services and the role of general practitioners

Research has shown consistently that families rarely refer themselves directly for services (Sinclair *et al.*, 1990) and the families in our study were no exception. Few carers had approached respite services directly for assistance. The majority of those without services had never asked for them, or were even necessarily aware of their existence. Now that local and health authorities publish information about their community care services in a more accessible and readily available form, this situation may change in the long term. Although recent years have seen a greater public awareness of Alzheimer's disease and related disorders, it is unrealistic to expect that potential carers will always approach services themselves. This accentuates the need for general practitioners and other primary care workers to be aware of people on their register or caseload who might be at risk and refer to specialist services when appropriate.

General practitioners are likely to remain a key point of entry into the care management system. It is essential that they are provided with clear information on the services available, the means of accessing them and that they are kept fully appraised of individual care plans and new local developments. This is all the more important in the light of pessimistic reports about general practitioners' and social workers' perceptions of the former's role in community care services (Ivory, 1993).

Clarifying the ways in which access to services is arranged is of vital importance in the light of our imperfect knowledge on the stage at which services can intervene most effectively. In Chapter Eight we noted that, in general, studies have reported only moderate effects of community services upon entry to residential care for people with dementia. It has been suggested by some commentators that, if it were possible to ensure that carers were offered services before levels of strain had built up, then this might lead to more positive findings.

In our study, at the time that they were first interviewed, the carers had been caring, on average, for about five years. Using the carers' estimates of onset, the mean length of time caring before day care, sitting or relief care had started was around four years. There was, in fact, enormous variation in these figures. Some carers had been identified at a very early stage. Others had been caring for several years with no respite services at all. One Scottish study found that approximately 10 per cent of people aged 75 and over with moderate to severe dementia were not known to any service provider (Carr, 1993). Only when there is less variability in the process by which carers and elderly people become known to community care services, will we be able to have a clearer idea of whether policies of early intervention can have a beneficial effect.

Integrating respite and other community services

We concluded that elderly people with dementia and their carers have a wide range of needs and difficulties which change over time. This is consistent with other studies (Kuhn, 1990). Services such as counselling and information may be most useful in the earlier stages of caring for a person with Alzheimer's disease or a related disorder. Services such as respite will assume greater relevance at later points.

Another example of the need to ensure that respite and other services are integrated is that of carers' groups. Almost 30 per cent of the carers had tried attending a group at least once but attendance was nearly always dependent upon what arrangements they could make for the care of the elderly person. It is essential to ensure that those people attending carers' groups have access to a sitting service, or a similar type of arrangement, to look after the person they care for.

Balancing community and residential provision

The aims of enabling people to remain in their own homes wherever possible and reducing the resources imbalance between residential and community care services are central to current policies. For resident carers who, even if it were to be offered, are less likely to find the idea of residential care acceptable, it is essential to recognise that they are disadvantaged by systems where residential provision considerably outweighs that for community based services.

If the elderly person had died by the time that we interviewed the carers for the second time, we asked whether he or she had spent time in residential care. This information is based only upon 79 cases of the 101 elderly people who died because, in addition to those cases where there was no second interview, some carers were unable to remember specific dates. Six of the elderly people had died at home. Among the rest, the mean time spent in residential or local authority homes, nursing homes and NHS hospitals prior to their death was just two months. This suggests that many people with diagnoses of Alzheimer's disease or a related disorder who have a resident carer may often be cared for at home right up until the most terminal stages of their condition.

Our final point is that residential and community services should be seen as complementary, not competing services. For some, service use enabled them to continue as carers. For others, it was used as a way of managing the process of ceasing to care. Therefore, we must accept that there is more than one purpose to respite services.

Suggestions for the future

Our final comments re-emphasise many of the themes throughout this book. We found, as we expected, that there was no single type and level of respite which would have suited all the carers. Individual carers and those for whom they cared had differing needs and strengths. Therefore, their needs for breaks varied according to circumstances, preferred leisure activities, and the personal care, supervision needs, and behavioural problems of the person cared for. Recent legislation has emphasised the importance of taking account of the views of carers and those using services. We now have an opportunity to see whether this will result in services becoming more effective.

Some carers arranged respite services from within their own network of family and friends and others arranged for help privately. The majority of carers in the sample relied mainly upon statutory or voluntary sources of help. Day, sitting and relief care services were relevant, valued highly and the carers believed that they benefited from them.

It is essential to respect carers' own perceptions of the services they require. Carers who felt unwilling or unable to continue caring at first interview were extremely unlikely to be still caring on follow up. Rather than pressurising such people to continue when this eventually may be to no avail, it may be more valuable to concentrate respite services on those who wish to continue.

This study has added to the existing body of research on the types of services wanted by carers. Whether their choices and preferences can ultimately influence the services which they are likely to receive is a question which can only be answered in the future.

References

Alzheimer's Disease Society (1993) *Deprivation and Dementia*, London: Alzheimer's Disease Society.

Age Concern (1992) *Standards in Day Care Services*, London: Age Concern England.

Allen, I. (1983) *Short Stay Residential Care for the Elderly*, London: Policy Studies Institute.

Allen, I., Hogg, D. and Peace, S. (1992) *Elderly People: Choice, Participation and Satisfaction*, London: Policy Studies Institute.

Arber, S. and Ginn, J. (1991) *Gender and Later Life*, London: Sage.

Askham, J., Barry, C., Grundy, E., Hancock, R. and Tinker, A. (1992) *Life After 60: a Profile of Britain's Older Population*, London: Age Concern Institute of Gerontology.

Audit Commision (1992) *The Community Revolution: Personal Social Services and Community Care*, London: HMSO.

Barry, N. (1988) Sitting tight - taking the strain for carers, *Social Work Today*, 19, 30.

Bird, A.S., Macdonald, A.J.D., Mann, A.H. and Philpott, M.P. (1987) Preliminary experience with the SELFCARE (D): a self-rating depression questionnaire for use in elderly, non-institutionalised subjects, *International Journal of Geriatric Psychiatry*, 2, 31-38.

Blessed, G., Black, S.E., Butler, T. and Kay, D.W.K. (1991) The diagnosis of dementia in the elderly: a comparison of CAMCOG, the AGECAT programs, DSM-III, the Mini Mental State Examination and some short rating scales, *British Journal of Psychiatry*, 159, 193-198.

Bowling, A., Farquar, M., Grundy, E. and Formby, J. (1992) *Psychiatric Morbidity among people aged 85+: a Follow Up Study*, London: Age Concern Institute of Gerontology.

Boardman, A.P. (1987) The General Health Questionnaire and the detection of emotional disorder by general practitioners: a replicated study, *British Journal of Psychiatry*, 151, 373–81.

Boldy, D. and Kuh, D. (1984) Short term care for the elderly in residential homes: a research note, *British Journal of Social Work*, 14, 173-175.

Borden, W. (1991) Stress, coping and adaptation in spouses of older adults with chronic dementia, *Social Work Research and Abstracts*, 27, 14-21.

[175]

Brearley P. and Mandelstam, M. (1991) *A Review of the Literature 1986-1991 on Day Care Services for Adults*, London: HMSO.

Bristow, A. (1986) *Cause for Concern: A Study of People Who Have the Ultimate Responsibility of Caring for a Severely Disabled and/or Elderly Person Living at Home*, Rugby: Association of Crossroads Care Attendant Schemes.

Brodaty, H. and Gresham, M. (1989) Effect of a training programme to reduce stress in carers of people with dementia, *British Medical Journal*, 299, 1375-1379.

Brodaty, H. and Gresham, M. (1992) Prescribing residential respite care for dementia - effects, side-effects, indications and dosage, *International Journal of Geriatric Psychiatry*, 7, 356-362.

Brody, E.M., Saperstein, A.R. and Powell Lawton, M. (1989) A multi-service respite program for caregivers of Alzheimer's patients, *Journal of Gerontological Social Work*, 14, 41-74.

Burningham, S. (1990) *Good Practice Booklet*, London: Alzheimer's Disease Society.

Burns, A., Jacoby, R. and Levy, R. (1990) Psychiatric phenomena in Alzheimer's Disease. iv: disorders of behaviour, *British Journal of Psychiatry*, 157, 86-94.

Callahan, J.J. (1989) Play it again Sam - there is no impact, *The Gerontologist*, 29, 5-6.

Carers National Association (1992) *Speak Up, Speak Out*, London: CNA.

Carr, J.S. (1992) *Tayside Dementia Services Planning Survey*, Stirling: Dementia Services Development Centre.

Central Statistical Office (1993) *Social Trends*, London: HMSO.

Challis, D. (1992) Providing alternatives to long-stay hospital care for frail elderly patients: is it cost-effective? *International Journal of Geriatric Psychiatry*, 7, 773-81.

Chappell, N. and Blandford, A. (1991) Informal and formal care: exploring the complementarity, *Ageing and Society*, 11, 299-317.

Children Act 1989 Ch. 48. (1989), London: HMSO.

Cullen, M., Blizard, R., Livingston, G. and Mann, A. (1992) *A Report on the Changes in Service Utilisation and Provision in the Gospel Oak Area of London over a Three Year Period from 1987-1990*, London: Royal Free Hospital Trust and Institute of Psychiatry.

Dalley, G. (1988) *Ideologies of Caring*, Basingstoke: Macmillan Education Ltd.

Dant, T. and Gearing, B. (1990) Key workers for elderly people in the community: case managers and care co-ordination, *Journal of Social Policy*, 19, 331-360.

Department of Health (1990) *Community Care in the Next Decade and Beyond*, London: HMSO.

Department of Health (1991) *Residential Accommodation for Elderly and for Younger Physically Handicapped People: All Residents in Local Authority Voluntary and Private Homes Year End 31 March 1990 (England)*, prepared by the Government Statistical Service RA/90/2, London: Department of Health.

Department of Health (1993) *Hospital Episode Statistics Volume 1, Finished Consultant Episodes by Diagnosis, Operation and Speciality, England: Financial year 1989–90, prepared by the GSS*, London: HMSO.

Department of Health/Social Services Inspectorate (1991a) *Complaints Procedures: Practice Guidance*, London: HMSO.

Department of Health/Social Services Inspectorate (1991b) *Community Care Plans: the First Steps*, London: HMSO.

Department of Health/Social Services Inspectorate (1991c) *Purchase of Service: Practice Guidance and Practice Material for Social Services Departments and Other Agencies*, London: HMSO.

Department of Health/Social Services Inspectorate (1991d) *Training for Community Care: a Joint Approach*, London: HMSO.

Donaldson, C., Clark, K., Gregson, B., Backhouse, M. and Pragnall, C. (1988) *Evaluation of a Family Support Unit for Elderly Mentally Infirm People and their Carers*, Newcastle: Health Care Research Unit Report 34.

Dunstan, E.J. (1989) Why does regular relief care end? *Age and Ageing*, 18, 201-204.

Eagles, J.M., Craig, A., Rawlinson, F., Restall D.B., Beattie, J.A.G. and Besson, J.A.O. (1987) The psychological well-being of supporters of the demented elderly, *British Journal of Psychiatry*, 150, 293-298.

Ehrlich, P. and White, J. (1991) TOPS: A consumer approach to Alzheimer's respite programs, *The Gerontologist*, 31, 686-691.

Farrow, G.N. (1992) The role of day centres in caring for people in the final year of their lives, *Ageing and Society*, 12, 313-327.

Finch, J. (1989) *Family Obligations and Social Change*, Cambridge: Polity Press.

Finch, J. and Groves, D. (eds.) (1983) *A Labour of Love: Women, Work and Caring*, London: Routledge.

Finch, J. and Mason, J. (1993) *Negotiating Family Responsibilities*, London: Routledge.

Gilhooly, M.L.M. (1984) The impact of care-giving on care-givers: factors associated with the psychological wellbeing of people supporting a dementing relative in the community. *British Journal of Medical Psychology*, 57, 35-44.

Gilleard, C.J. (1984) *Living with Dementia: Community Care of the Elderly Mentally Infirm*, London: Croom Helm.

Gilleard, C.J. (1987) Influence of emotional distress among supporters on the outcome of psychogeriatric day care, *British Journal of Psychiatry*, 150, 219-223.

Gilleard, C.J. (1992) Community Care Services for the Elderly Mentally Ill, in Jones, G.M.M. and Mieson, B.M.L., *Care-giving in Dementia: Research and Applications*, London: Routledge.

Gilleard, C.J., Belford, H., Gilleard, E., Whittick, J.E. and Gledhill, K. (1984) Emotional distress amongst the supporters of the elderly mentally infirm, *British Journal of Psychiatry*, 145, 172-177.

Gilleard, C.J., Gilleard, E. and Whittick, J.E. (1984) Impact of a psychogeriatric day hospital on the patient's family, *British Journal of Psychiatry*, 145, 487-492.

Glendinning, C. (1992) *The Costs of Informal Care: Looking Inside the Household*, London: HMSO.

Goldberg, D. (1978) *Manual of General Health Questionnaire*, Windsor: National Federation of Educational Research Publishing Company.

Goldberg, D. and Williams, P. (1988) *A User's Guide to the General Health Questionnaire*, Windsor: NFER-Nelson Publishing Company.

Green, H. (1988) *Informal Carers*, OPCS Series GHS, No. 15, Supplement A, London: HMSO.

Griffith, D. (1993) Respite care should be made less difficult, *British Medical Journal*, 306, 160.

Grundy, E. and Harrop, A. (1992) Co-residence between adult children and their elderly parents in England and Wales, *Journal of Social Policy*, 21, 325-348.

Gwyther, L.P. (1989) Overcoming barriers: home care for dementia sufferers, *Caring*, August, 12-16.

Gwyther, L.P. and George, L.K. (1986) Caregiver well-being: a multidimensional examination of family caregivers of demented adults, *The Gerontologist*, 26, 253-259.

Haffenden, S. (1991) *Getting it Right for Carers*, London: HMSO.

Harper, D.J., Manasse, P.R., James, O. and Newton, J.T. (1993) Intervening to reduce distress in caregivers of impaired elderly people: a preliminary evaluation, *International Journal of Geriatric Psychiatry*, 8, 139-145.

Hart, M. (1991) *Not Enough Care: A Report on a Canvass of Carers and their Use of Respite Care Services*, London: Alzheimer's Disease Society.

Hinchcliffe, A.C., Hyman, I., Blizard, B. and Livingston, G. (1992) The impact on carers of behavioural difficulties in dementia: a pilot study of management, *International Journal of Geriatric Psychiatry*, 7, 579-583.

Homer, A.C. and Gilleard, C. (1990) Abuse of elderly people by their carers, *British Medical Journal*, 301, 1359-1362.

House of Commons Social Services Committee (1990) *Community Care: Carers (Fifth Report)*, London: HMSO.

Iliffe, S., Booroff, A., Gallivan, S., Goldenberg, E., Morgan, P. and Haines, A. (1990) Screening for cognitive impairment in the elderly using the mini-mental state examinations, *British Journal of General Practice*, 40, 277-79.

Illsley, J. (1992) *The Govan Dementia Project - Day and Night Care,* Stirling: Dementia Services Development Centre.

Ivory, M. (1993) Can the rift be healed? *Community Care,* Issue 960, 1 April 1993.

Jones, D.A. and Salvage, A.V. (1992) Attitudes to caring among a group of informal carers of elderly dependents, *Archives of Gerontology and Geriatrics,* 14, 155-65.

Jorm, A.F. and Korten, A.E. (1988) A method for calculating projected increases in the number of dementia sufferers, *Australian and New Zealand Journal of Psychiatry,* 22, 183-89.

Katona, C.L.E. and Aldridge, C.R. (1985) The dexamethasone suppression test and depressive signs in dementia, *Journal of Affective Disorders,* 8, 83-89.

Kuhn, D.R. (1990) The normative crises of families confronting dementia, *Families in Society,* 71, 451-459.

Lawton, M.P., Brody, E.M. and Saperstein, A.R. (1989) A controlled study of respite services for caregivers of Alzheimer's patients, *The Gerontologist,* 29, 8-16.

Leat, D. (1992) Innovations and special schemes, in Twigg, J. *Carers Research and Practice,* London: HMSO.

Lennon, S. and Jolley, D. (1991) An urban service in South Manchester, in Jacoby, R. and Oppenheimer, C. *Psychiatry in the Elderly,* Oxford: Oxford University Press, 322-388.

Levin, E. and Moriarty, J. (1990) *Ready to Cope Again: Sitting, Day and Relief Care for the Carers of Confused Elderly People,* Interim Report to DH, London: National Institute for Social Work.

Levin, E., Moriarty, J. and Gorbach, P. (1992) *I Couldn't Manage Without the Breaks,* Draft Report to DH, London: National Institute for Social Work.

Levin, E., Sinclair, I. and Gorbach, P. (1989) *Families, Services and Confusion in Old Age,* Aldershot: Gower.

Lewis, J. and Meredith, B. (1988) *Daughters Who Care: Daughters Caring for Mothers at Home,* London: Routledge.

Lieberman, M.A. and Kramer, J.H. (1991) Factors affecting decisions to institutionalise demented elderly, *The Gerontologist,* 31, 371-374.

Livingston, G., Thomas, A., Graham, N., Blizard, B. and Mann, A. (1990) The Gospel Oak Project: the use of health and social services by dependent elderly people in the community, *Health Trends,* 22, 70-73.

Lodge, B. (1990) *Alternative Homes for People with Dementia: New Directions in Service Principles and Design,* Stoke on Trent: British Association for Services for the Elderly.

Lodge, B. (1991) *Whither Now? Planning Services for People with Dementia,* Stoke on Trent: British Association for Services for the Elderly.

McCreadie, C. (1991) *Elder Abuse: an Exploratory Study,* London: Age Concern Institute of Gerontology.

McLaughlin, E. (1991) *Social Security and Community Care: the Case of the Invalid Care Allowance*, Department of Social Security Research Report no. 4, London: HMSO.

Martinus, P. and Severs, M. (1988) Quantifying the effects of respite care, *Geriatric Medicine*, 18, 10, 73-79.

Melzer, D. (1990) An evaluation of a respite care unit for elderly people with dementia: framework and some results, *Health Trends*, 22, 2, 64-67.

Miller, B. and Cafassa, L. (1992) Gender differences in caregiving: fact or artifact? *The Gerontologist*, 32, 498-507.

Montgomery, R.V.J. and Borgatta E.F. (1989) The effects of alternative support strategies on family caregiving, *The Gerontologist*, 29, 457-464.

Moriarty, J. and Levin, E. (1993) Services to people with dementia and their carers, in Burns, A. *Ageing and Dementia - A Methodological Approach*, Sevenoaks: Edward Arnold.

Moriarty, J. and Levin, E. (1993) Interventions to assist caregivers, *Reviews in Clinical Gerontology*, 3 01-308.

Morris, R., Morris, L.W. and Britton, P.G. (1989) Factors affecting the wellbeing of the caregivers of dementia sufferers, *British Journal of Psychiatry*, 153, 147-156.

Mui, A.C. (1992) Caregiver strain among black and white daughter caregivers: a role theory perspective, *The Gerontologist*, 32, 203-212.

Murphy, E. (1986) *Dementia and Mental Illness in the Old*, London: Macmillan.

National Health Service and Community Care Act 1990 Ch. 19 (1990) London: HMSO.

Nies, H., Tester, S. and Nuijens, J.M. (1991) Day care in the United Kingdom and the Netherlands: a comparative study, *Ageing and Society*, 11, 245-273.

Noelker, L.N. and Bass, D.M. (1989) Home care for elderly persons: linkages between formal and informal caregivers, *Journal of Gerontology*, 44, 2, S63-70.

Nolan, M. and Grant, G. (1992) *Regular Respite: an Evaluation of a Hospital Rota Bed Scheme for Elderly People*, London: Age Concern.

Office of Population Censuses and Surveys (1988) *The Prevalence of Disability among Adults*, London: HMSO.

Office of Population Censuses and Surveys (Foster, K., Wilmot, A. and Dobbs, J.) (1990) *General Household Survey 1988*, London: HMSO.

Ogg, J. and Bennett, G. (1992) Elder abuse in Britain, *British Medical Journal*, 305, 998-999.

Opit, L. and Pahl, J. (1993) Institutional care for elderly people: can we predict admissions? *Research, Policy and Planning*, 10, 2-5.

O'Connor, D.W., Pollitt, P.A., Brook, C.P.B. and Reiss, B.B (1989) The distribution of services to demented elderly people living in the community, *International Journal of Geriatric Psychiatry*, 4, 339-44.

O'Connor, D.W., Pollitt, P.A., Brook, C.P.B., Reiss, B.B. and Roth, M. (1991) Does early intervention reduce the number of elderly people with dementia admitted to institutions for long term care? *British Medical Journal*, 302, 871-5.

O'Connor, D.W., Pollitt, P.A., Hyde, J.B., Brook, C.P.B. and Roth, M. (1988) Do general practitioners miss dementia in elderly patients? *British Medical Journal*, 297, 1107-10.

O'Connor, D.W., Pollitt, P.A., Roth, M., Brook C.P.B. and Reiss, B.B. (1990) Problems reported by relatives in a community study of dementia, *British Journal of Psychiatry*, 156, 835-41.

Pahl, J. (1989a) *Money and Marriage*, Basingstoke: Macmillan Education Ltd.

Pahl, J. (1989b) Day services for elderly people: some misunderstandings and mixed metaphors, in Morton, J. (ed.) *New Approaches to Day Care for Elderly People*, London: Age Concern Institute of Gerontology.

Parker, G. (1990) *With Due Care and Attention: A Review of Research on Informal Care*, London: Family Policy Studies Centre.

Parker, G. (1992) Counting care: numbers and types of informal carers, in Twigg, J. *Carers, Research and Practice*, London: HMSO.

Parks, S.H. and Pilisuk, M. (1991) Caregiver burden: gender and the psychological costs of caregiving, *American Journal of Orthopsychiatry*, 61, 501-509.

Pattie, A.H. and Gilleard, C.J. (1979) *Manual of the Clifton Assessment Procedures for the Elderly*, Kent: Hodder and Stoughton.

Pattie, A.H. and Heaton, J. (1990) A Comparative Study of Dependency and Provision of Care in the State and Private Sector in York Health District, cited in Henwood, M. (1992) *Through a Glass Darkly*, London: Kings Fund Institute.

Paveza, G.J., Cohen, D., Eisdorfer, C., Freels, S., Semla, T., Ashford, J.W., Gorelick, P., Hirschman, R., Luchins, D. and Levy, P. (1992) Severe family violence and Alzheimer's Disease: prevalence and risk factors, *The Gerontologist*, 32, 493-497.

Payne, C. (ed.) (1989) *Better Services for Older People*, London: National Institute for Social Work.

Pearlin, L.I., Mullan, J.T., Semple, S.J. and Skaff, M.M. (1990) Caregiving and the stress process: an overview of concepts and their measures, *The Gerontologist*, 30, 583-591.

Pearson, N.D. (1988) An assessment of relief hospital admissions for elderly patients with dementia, *Health Trends*, 20, 120-121.

Personal Service Society (1993) *Yearbook*, Liverpool: Personal Service Society.

Philp, I. and Young, J. (1988) An audit of a primary care team's knowledge of the existence of symptomatic demented elderly, *Health Bulletin*, 46, 93-7.

Primrose, C.S. and Primrose, W.R. (1992) Geriatric respite care - present practice and scope for improvement, *Health Bulletin*, 50, 399-406.

Qureshi, H. and Walker, A. (1989) *The Caring Relationship: Elderly People and their Families*, Basingstoke: Macmillan Education Ltd.

Rai, G.S., Bielawska, C., Murphy, P.J. and Wright, G. (1986) Hazards for elderly people admitted for respite (holiday admissions) and social care (social admissions), *British Medical Journal*, 292, 240.

Reddy, S. and Pitt, B. (1993) 'What becomes of demented patients referred to a psychogeriatric unit?' An approach to audit, *International Journal of Geriatric Psychiatry*, 8, 175-180.

Reid, G. (1992) *Making Belfast Work: The North and West Belfast Dementia Project*, Belfast: Department of Health and Social Services (Northern Ireland).

Ritchie, K. (1992) Life expectancy without cognitive deterioration: theoretical and methodological difficulties, in Robine, J.M. Blanchet, M., and Dowd, J.E., Office of Population Censuses and Surveys *Studies on Medical and Population Subjects Number 54 Health Expectancy*, London: HMSO.

Ritchie, K. and Ledésert, B. (1992) The families of the instituionalized dementing elderly: a preliminary study of stress in a French caregiver population, *International Journal of Geriatric Psychiatry*, 7, 5-14.

Robbins, D. (ed.) (1993) *Community Care: Findings from Department of Health Funded Research 1988-1992*, London: HMSO.

Robinson, C. (1991) *Home and Away: Respite Care in the Community*, Birmingham: Venture Press.

Rosenvinge, H., Guion, J. and Dawson, J. (1986) Sitting service for the elderly confused: part of an integrated programme of management, *Health Trends*, 18, 47.

Salter, C. (1992) The day centre: a way of avoiding society's risk, *Critical Public Health*, 3, 17-22.

Secretaries of State (1989) *Caring for People*, London: HMSO.

Scharlach, A. and Frenzel, C. (1986) An evaluation of institution based respite care, *The Gerontologist*, 26, 77-82.

Sinclair, I., Parker, R., Leat, D. and Williams, J. (1990) *The Kaleidoscope of Care*, London: HMSO.

Sistler, A. (1989) Adaptive coping of older caregiving spouses, *Social Work*, 34, 415-420.

Social Services Inspectorate (1993) *Caring for Quality in Day Care Services*, London: HMSO.

Social Services Inspectorate (1992) *Confronting Elder Abuse*, London: HMSO.

Social Services Inpectorate (1993) *Guidance on Standards for Short Term Breaks*, London: HMSO.

Social Services Inspectorate/Scottish Office Social Work Service Group (1991a) *Care Management and Assessment: Managers' Guide*, London: HMSO.

Social Services Inspectorate/Scottish Office Social Work Service Group (1991b) *Care Management and Assessment: Practitioners' Guide*, London: HMSO.

Springer, D. and Brubaker, T.H. (1984) *Family Caregivers and Dependent Elderly: Minimizing Stress and Maximizing Independence*, Sage: Newbury Park.

Tester, S. (1989) *Caring by Day: a Study of Day Care Services for Older People*, London: Centre for Policy on Ageing.

Thornton, P. (1989) *Creating a Break: A Home Care Relief Scheme for Elderly People and their Supporters*, Mitcham: Age Concern.

Twigg, J. (1992) Carers in the Service System, in Twigg, J. *Carers Research and Practice* London: HMSO.

Twigg, J. and Atkin, K. (1991) *Evaluating Support to Informal Carers: Summary Report*, York: Social Policy Research Unit.

Twigg, J., Atkin, K. and Perring, C. (1990) *Carers and Services: A Review of Research*, London: HMSO.

Tym, E. (1991) A rural service in East Anglia in Jacoby, R. and Oppenheimer, C. *Psychiatry in the Elderly*, Oxford: Oxford University Press.

Ungerson C. (1987) *Policy is Personal*, London: Tavistock.

Vetter, N.J., Lewis, P.A. and Llewellyn, L. (1992) Supporting elderly dependent people at home, *British Medical Journal*, 304, 1290-1292.

Vitaliano, P.P., Young, H.M. and Russo, J. (1991) A review of measures used among caregivers of individuals with dementia, *The Gerontologist*, 31, 67-75.

Weaver, T., Willcocks, D. and Kellaher, L. (1985) The business of care: a study of private residential homes for old people, cited in Twigg, J., Atkin, K. and Perring, C. *Carers and Services*, London: HMSO.

Wells, Y.D., Jorm, A.F., (1987) Evaluation of a special nursing home unit for dementia sufferers, *Australian and New Zealand Journal of Psychiatry*, 21, 524-531.

Wells, Y.D., Jorm, A.F., Jordan, F. and Lefroy, R. (1990) Effects on care-givers of special day care programmes for dementia sufferers, *Australian and New Zealand Journal of Psychiatry*, 24, 1-9.

Wenger G.C. (1992) *Help in Old Age - Facing up to Change*, Occasional Paper 5. Liverpool: Liverpool University Press.

Wyn Thomas, B. (1990) *Consulting Consumers in the NHS: a Guideline Study Services for Elderly People with Dementia Living at Home*, London: National Consumer Council.

Zarit, S. and Teri, L. (1991) Interventions and services for family caregivers, *Annual Review of Gerontology and Geriatrics*, 11, 287-310.

Subject Index

Index of works cited

Printed in the United Kingdom for HMSO
Dd. 0297109 2/94 C25 531/3 12521